This Book Belongs To:

Fairy Tale Review

The Rainbow Issue

Founding Editor
Kate Bernheimer, Professor, University of Arizona

Editor
Benjamin Schaefer

Poetry Editor
Jon Riccio

Advisory Board
Donald Haase, Wayne State University
Maria Tatar, Harvard University
Jack Zipes, University of Minnesota

Associate Prose Editor
Wendy Oleson

Associate Poetry Editors
Adam Al-Sirgany
Nazli Pearl
Matthew Schmidt
Billie R. Tadros

Original Print Design
J. Johnson, DesignFarm

Cover Art (Inside Frame)
Kiki Smith, "Born"
Courtesy of the Artist

Layout
Andrew Katz

FAIRY TALE REVIEW

FAIRY TALE REVIEW is devoted to publishing contemporary fairy tales and new translations of fairy tales into English. We are interested in the aesthetics and ethics of fairy tales and in diverse styles and forms—we seek to nurture the many voices of fairy tales through an inclusive atmosphere. How can fairy tales help us to go where it is we are going, like Jean Cocteau's magical horse? We hope to learn. FAIRY TALE REVIEW was founded in 2005.

FAIRY TALE REVIEW is published annually in March by Wayne State University Press.
Subscription correspondence should be addressed to:
Wayne State University Press
Leonard N. Simons Building
4809 Woodward Avenue
Detroit, Michigan 48201-1309
Toll-free phone number: 1-800-WSU-READ

All editorial correspondence should be addressed to:
Kate Bernheimer, Editor
FAIRY TALE REVIEW
E-mail address: ftreditorial@gmail.com
Website: www.fairytalereview.com

For ordering information, visit our website: wsupress.wayne.edu

Annual subscription rates for print, effective with The Rainbow Issue, Volume 19:
For individuals, $16.00 per year.
For institutions, $50.00 per year.

Postage: For AIR foreign postage, please add $18.00 to subscription rate.

Online and Print + Online subscriptions (for one issue and 12-month access):
For institutions, contact Project MUSE for pricing.

Back-issue rates: The Blue Issue, Volume 1 (2005) through The Lilac Issue, Volume 18 (2022) are available from Wayne State University Press at the following rates:
For individuals and students/seniors, $16.00 per issue.
For institutions, $50.00 per issue.

Bulk orders are available at a discount.
For more information, contact Journals Order Fulfillment at 1-313-577-4603.
Journal Subscriptions fax number: 1-313-577-6131

Copyright © 2023 Wayne State University Press, Leonard N. Simons Building, Detroit, Michigan 48201-1309. ISSN: 1556-6153.

The rainbow icon that appears throughout this issue is Rainbow by Anna Nebbiati from the Noun Project.

"We gays cast our nets out into the mythic sea, searching for our own lost archetypes . . . those symbols of the human psyche which we may claim as emblematic of our own particular way of being."

—Stanley Johnson, "On the Banks of the River Time Looking Inland"

Fairy Tale Review

The Rainbow Issue

ANNOTATED TABLE OF CONTENTS

Benjamin Schaefer
Editor's Note · 15

Fairy tales, with their intuitive logic and normalized magic, have always been at odds with a certain school of literary realism, and yet I would argue they remain humanity's longest-standing storytelling tradition precisely because of their ability to render lived human experience despite their apparent detachment from reality. They are both themselves queer *and* a place where queerness can speak and thrive and live.

Shastri Akella
The Magic Bangle · 20

Kartik makes a decision the day his father strikes him: on workday evenings and weekends he'll pretend he's a tourist in his hometown. His real home—where he belongs—is a place, he imagines, where it's safe for him to love men.

MARY ANGELINO
Dear Girlhood · 28

First, she felt it thin and shrink
like a child caught in a lie,
so she took it off and carried it.
Please don't ask how she looked

underneath (like a child caught in a lie)

CLAYTON BRADSHAW
The Ungrateful Dead · 32

The same summer the San Antonio Spurs defeat the Miami Heat in Game 5 of the NBA Finals, Robin Williams hangs himself in his final act of ironic comedy, the Philae lander tumbles towards its fateful rendezvous with the Churyumov-Gerasimenko comet, and an overheated Eric Garner dies breathless in a chokehold, Grayce stands before the judge in Homerville, Georgia, and declares: Greg Clarkson is dead. I killed him.

ROBERT CARR
At the Hatter's Table · 41

Edible. Sometimes. Cool
Whip, dream whip, buttercream,

butter stick, sweet and sour, fruit
spread, cocoa on my junk.

Anna Graeme
sphinx women · 42

Sphinx women find jobs on the street
as women who sell fruit and bright clothes
and handmade jewelry.

Hannah Grieco
If you were red riding hood · 43

and I found you, sniffed you out on the path with your basket, your cape, your soft hair, your pink-orange freckles lit by the sun piercing the canopy, and if I jumped out, held up my thick paws and clipped nails, opened my mouth wide, to show not teeth but hunger, not teeth but patience, as you walked this forest over and over

Allegra Hyde
A Whale Tale · 44

The whale was already dead when it washed ashore. A massive sperm whale, its skin leathery and barnacled, its narrow jaw strutted with teeth. The whole town went down to the beach to see it: mothers and firefighters and stay-at-home dads and dead-beat dads and vacuum cleaner salespeople and endometriologists and dowagers and women of the night and diamond miners and fortune tellers and personal trainers. Children were bussed in from school. Prisoners from prison. Altogether, the townspeople encircled the creature, reaching forward to touch its gray-blue skin.

Catherine Kim

The Fox Marble · *50*

From the overlook, Yeou could see the stretch of the village below her, from the paddy fields by the base of the mountain to the bus terminal at its furthest reach. With a finger outstretched towards the vanishing point, she could trace the road as it split from the highway and flowed into the village, winding around the homes, the crop fields, the greenhouses, and the livestock pens, past the irrigation pond and up the slope towards her perch.

Kyle Marbut

Four Poems from Black Swan Theory · *59*

Dressed in just your blue jockstrap, you come to me whirling through the graveyard. Bearing honeycomb and black lace veils, foam at the mouth. Not the moonlight but what's beneath it makes the night real.

Mike McClelland

Is the Sky Falling or Are We Rising Towards the Lord? · *63*

The first church to ascend rose in rambling loops, slow but determined, a beanstalk growing towards the sun. Many followed, sometimes as many as forty or fifty churches in a day, though it appeared only one church per town made the cut. This seemed terribly unfair, particularly when Bezaleel, New Jersey's one rickety steeple took off on the same day as Manhattan's 23rd Street Synagogue.

Christopher Nelson
Theology · 76

said the blade to the lamb we're in this together said the garden to the god when do we have a say said the lamb in return yes but only one of us is an exit

Reuben Gelley Newman
Dear Dear · 77

The dog-eared copy of *Autobiography of Red*
seemed like something archival to him,
smudged with the fingerprints of who knows how many boys
and perhaps some charcoal and semen,
so of course he lingered in the library with the Hershey's Kisses
left over from Valentine's Day

Carolyn Oliver
From Her Tulip Bower Tommelise Writes the Swallow · 81

Dear Swallow, how is a hollow mended?
The gilded wings he pledged were barely floss
enough to lift a raindrop's song. He fed me wind
and bone. Starved, I learned to swim.

Cat Powell
What's He Building in There · 83

Your father has been spending a lot of time in the basement recently, and I'm hoping you will speak with him about this. I know you keep saying you won't get involved in things between us anymore, but he is your father and I am concerned.

VAL RIGODON
Lipshine #18 Champagne Gold · 105

We could watch the moonrise from the pool, float on our backs, and count the silver spacecrafts puttering across the watercolor sky, striping it with seafoam-colored chemtrails, but you roll your eyes.

ZAK SALIH
The Death of Alexander the Great · 107

When they pass Mr. Nestor's house, Mike asks his parents to turn on WMMS. A boy again, at twenty-one, in the backseat of his parents' car, his own car in the front drive with its broken transmission, asking Mom and Dad to play some music.

ALYSIA LI YING SAWCHYN
Transfigure/Transform/Transmogrify · 121
An Essay

I dreamt about a castle; I dreamt I *was* a castle. Dreams are funny like that. A thing can look like or be something else entirely. Your pet cat appears before you as an extinct woodland bird, and though you've never owned a pair of binoculars or bought feeder seed, you are absolutely certain of the avian species and are, simultaneously, confident that it *is* your cat. The question *why*? never crosses your sleeping mind.

TIMOTHY SCHAFFERT
Dedication · 124

This one's for Mr. XXX in tiny italics
Who knocked at my choppers until I shut up,
the sentiment,
typically tucked in between title and stanza,
is the part of the poem I lick away first

JD Scott
The Selkie of the City Tells All · 126

We meet at the Mermaid Parade on Coney Island three years in a row. We meet on a rooftop on the Fourth of July, the air smoky with bodega-bought salutes. We meet on a broken-down B3 bus on Avenue U. We meet in front of Macy's between holidays, the arm of an animatronic elf waving in the window display.

Preston Smith
Narcissus Buys a Waterbed to Sleep with Himself · 129

If you feel you're being watched, you are
not alone.

Addie Tsai
Deep Sea Baby, I Follow You · 130

You cannot tell them. You cannot tell your five divine sisters, each as perfectly beautiful as the one before. You cannot tell your grandmother, whose heart would sink to the sea floor like a strange and unwanted anchor. You cannot tell your father, who has relied on you to be exactly as he has carved you to be, the image of his beloved who now resides in Heaven. You cannot tell any of them that who you are in your heart is not who stands before them in their eyes.

Michael Vargas
The Magician wears a tilma · 132

Sometimes I want what Diego had,
or at least
what all the artists, ethnoarcheologists, and clairvoyants
said
a shawl too drab for possession

Jae Towle Vieira
A Figure of Heroic Size · 134

In Katie's hometown—Auburn, California—the scales have been missing from the Ladies of Justice at the courthouse for more than one hundred years. Each of the three statues presides over a cardinal direction. None blindfolded, but none with pupils. All grip modest swords in their right hands, and all their lefts are extended as if to hand back change.

Contributor Notes & Artist Statements · 141

BENJAMIN SCHAEFER

Editor's Note

At the height of the COVID shutdown in the United States, I was asked to speak at an informal recovery meeting by a friend I had met ten years earlier in a twelve-step fellowship in Boston, Massachusetts. I got sober relatively young, at the age of twenty-four, and have remained sober and active in twelve-step recovery since October 26, 2008. Sobriety has been the singular blessing of my life, and in my time in recovery I've witnessed miraculous things occur in my life and the lives of other recovering people. And yet, to this day, one of the most impressive remains watching how quickly and efficiently the recovery community moved online in the early days of the shutdown. Within a week I could go to meetings all over the country, all over the world, with other people who were making it their business to stay sober a day at a time amidst the most cataclysmic event of our lifetimes. Never before had recovery felt so democratic.

But when my friend asked me to speak, I was reluctant. I was just then coming off a period of intensely painful emotional and spiritual growth—what we might call in recovery a spiritual awakening, but which had felt at the time more like a crisis of confidence. In the slow and quiet days of that summer's isolation, I had realized that at some point in my early sobriety I had developed certain ways of operating in the world to keep myself safe—particularly in my intimate relationships with men—but which had ultimately left me unseen. And I had wanted so badly to be seen. At twelve years sober, this was a difficult truth to reckon with, and in the aftermath of its revelation, I felt like cellophane: thin and transparent. But I agreed to speak at the meeting, because he was my friend and he had asked.

Logging onto the meeting, I was nervous. By that point in my recovery, I had shared at more meetings than I could possibly count, but I was still adjusting to sharing online where I couldn't gauge the feel of a room in quite the same way I could in person. I watched, slightly horrified, as more and more people signed into the meeting—people from Madison, Wisconsin, and Fort Lauderdale, Florida, and Southern California and New York City. Soon the number of participants reached more than eighty.

The meeting began and my friend introduced me. I read from a piece of recovery literature and then spoke for fifteen or twenty minutes about my experience in sobriety, after which the meeting opened for other people to share. It wasn't long before I realized that a large contingent of the meeting was made up of gay men. This was something of a revelation. Though there is a robust recovery community in my hometown, with more than three hundred meetings each week, only two are designated as queer meetings, and I had largely avoided those meetings throughout my sobriety for reasons that weren't entirely clear to me at the time, but which undoubtedly had to do with my own history of sexual trauma and my general distrust of men. But listening to those men share at that online meeting, I felt a familiar mixture of discomfort and curiosity. It was the peculiar emotional cocktail I've come to recognize as an invitation for further spiritual growth. The Universe was trying to tell me I had something more to learn. And so I began attending that meeting, which met every night during the pandemic, regularly.

It was at that meeting that I met a gay actor who was weathering the shutdown in Stamford, Connecticut, and who had been sober for almost three years. We embarked on a deep and abiding friendship. Every night after the meeting, we'd talk on the phone, sometimes for hours. During one of these phone calls, this man told me he had once heard someone describe recovery as a journey towards becoming whole, but that something about that framing didn't feel right to him. It was a subject I had given a lot of thought, both in my recovery and during my years teaching mindfulness practice for an Internet startup. I told my friend that the problem with that statement was that it implied that at some point we are not whole. But we are never not whole. We are born whole. Wholeness is our birthright. And yes, there are certainly times when we *lose sight* of our wholeness. All kinds of things can get in the way of us seeing and knowing and believing it: trauma, addiction, misogyny, racism, poverty, neglect, illness—to name a few. But that doesn't mean we are ever not whole. "Recovery is not a journey towards *becoming* whole," I told him. "It is a journey towards *experiencing* our wholeness." After that previous summer's painful revelation, it was a reminder I myself needed to hear.

Eventually the shutdown ended, in-person meetings resumed, and my friend the actor and I returned to the busyness of our lives and our separate geographies. But still, I revisited our conversation about wholeness again and again in the years that followed, often in dialogue with my friends and fellow queer writers and editors Cat Powell and Taymour Soomro. We discussed wholeness as it related to queer representation in literature. It seemed to us that the queer narratives that gained the most traction with the mainstream were often narratives about the queer struggle for worthiness and belonging. In other words, they were narratives of *becoming*, rather than narratives of *being*. What would a body of queer literature look like, we wondered, if it originated from (rather than ended at) a place of wholeness? What responsibility did we as queer writers and editors and teachers have to usher that work into being? In hindsight, I am certain that it was these conversations that led me to pitch the idea of a queer-themed issue of *Fairy Tale Review* to the journal's Founding Editor, Kate Bernheimer.

Fairy tales have always struck me as an inherently queer art form—though I guess that depends on one's definition of queerness. I think of the writer and activist bell hooks who, in a conversation at Eugene Lang College in 2014, defined queerness as "the self that is at odds with everything around it and has to invent and create and find a place to speak and to thrive and to live." What I love most about hooks's definition is that the emphasis is not on a *self* that needs to be invented, created, or found, but rather a *place* in which the queer self can be accommodated. Fairy tales, with their intuitive logic and normalized magic, have always been at odds with a certain school of literary realism, and yet I would argue they remain humanity's longest-standing storytelling tradition precisely because of their ability to render lived human experience despite their apparent detachment from reality. They are both themselves queer *and* a place where queerness can speak and thrive and live.

As we began formulating plans for The Rainbow Issue, which would feature queer fairy tales written exclusively by queer writers and writers who identified as members of the LGBTQIA+ community, I continued to puzzle over the relationship between wholeness and queerness and the fabulist tradition. I felt they were connected, but I couldn't yet articulate how. The answer came in an early brainstorming session I had with Kate Bernheimer, during which Kate quoted from an essay she had written on fairy tales and trauma. "Retelling is an act of reparation," she said. The comment stopped me cold. This was the key. To re-tell—that is, to tell a story previously told *anew*—is to re-pair. To join again two things that belong together. It was a lesson I had first learned in twelve-step meetings, where I sat and listened to people share their stories day after day, year after year. As I stayed sober and began to share my own story, something magical happened: my perspective and understanding of it evolved. I began to reframe it through the stories I heard others tell; I made connections I hadn't seen before—at a year sober, or five years, or eight, or twelve. And in the process, I learned to form a coherent narrative of my life, one in which every element of my story was integrated. The same could be said about fairy tales. Fairy tales have the power to restore us to an experience of our wholeness because in *retelling* them—telling them anew—we have the opportunity to reclaim authority over our oldest and most entrenched stories. Which is another way of saying we have the opportunity to reclaim authority over our lives. Fairy tales, too, are an act of recovery.

Imagine my surprise then, when reviewing the final manuscript of The Rainbow Issue, I noticed that the majority of its contents had one thing in common: apart from being queer, nearly all of them involved some kind of transformation. People transformed into castles and cakes and whole cities; they transformed into foxes and sphinxes, bears and wolves, daffodils and tobacco and cannabis. They transformed into reflections of their own mothers; they transformed into kings and spontaneous hustlers. I began to panic. "Oh no," I thought. "Are these narratives of *becoming*?" My panic was short-lived, however, when I realized how many of these transformations were physical. I remembered that for queer people—and women and BIPOC and people with disabilities—the journey towards an experience of our wholeness always begins with our bodies. It is our bodies that are often at odds with everything around them—that is to say, they are at odds with the patriarchy and majority culture—but they are also the place from which we must learn to speak and to thrive and to live wholly. Our bodies are the vessels that house our stories—stories not of our becoming, but of our being.

It has been the great privilege of my editorial career to serve as Editor for this special issue of *Fairy Tale Review*, and I am beyond grateful to Kate

Bernheimer and Poetry Editor Jon Riccio for affording me the opportunity, as well as to our editorial staff and all our contributors. And to you, our readers. The Rainbow Issue is a place that's now yours.

—Benjamin Schaefer
Editor
Rochester, NY

SHASTRI AKELLA

The Magic Bangle

Kartik makes a decision the day his father strikes him: on workday evenings and weekends he'll pretend he's a tourist in his hometown. His real home—where he belongs—is a place, he imagines, where it's safe for him to love men.

That Thursday after work he visits the Golconda Fort. He enlists the services of a tour guide, who takes him from the watchtower on the rampart to the courtroom in the heart of the fort. The tour guide tells Kartik about the fort's many tricks. Alcoves for soldiers to hide in plain sight. Unseen vantage points from which to pour hot oil on intruders. Kartik likes the clap trick best. When the watchtower soldier clapped, the sound traveled all the way to the courtroom: two claps for an approaching friend, one clap for a foe.

A happy future is the sound of two claps, Kartik thinks.

On Friday he tells his parents he's going to the Delhi office on a work trip and leaves home with a suitcase. At work he tells his colleagues he's going to see the Taj Mahal for the long weekend. The office will be closed on Monday for Holi.

He takes an Uber to his hometown's old district and checks into a hotel. His fourth-floor room has a balcony that overlooks the Charminar. He changes into a red kurta, straps his camera across his shoulder, and goes down to join the street traffic: scooterists, pedestrians, buffaloes, and peddlers of steel vessels, velvet pursers, and plastic roses. The air smells of jasmine and stagnant water. He crosses the Jama Masjid, whose stone courtyard is packed with Friday devotees. Men in kurtas lean towards one another, haloed in dusk's violet glow, their murmurs a collective buzz. The women's praying quarters, he guesses, are tucked away, out of sight.

He takes a right and enters the Bangle Bazaar. He pauses frequently to click a photograph. In a shop empty of customers, a man sitting behind the counter holds his attention. Camera to one eye, Kartik zooms in on him: his face in profile, illuminated by phone light, his skin the color of chai. A manicured stubble dots his angular jaw. There's a slight shift in his posture, as if he knows he's being watched. Not immediately, but at length, he lifts his head and looks. Kartik hones in on the man's green eyes, framed by his thick lashes, punctuated by a mole on his temple. *Click.* Kartik lowers his camera and walks into the shop. He occupies the chair the green-eyed stranger points to.

What kind of bangles are you looking for? the man asks Kartik. Glass? Enamel? Metal?

He speaks a mixture of Urdu and Hindi, and his voice brings to mind the sound of a stone skimming the surface of water.

What do you recommend? Kartik asks, holding one hand up. He points to his wrist.

The man rubs his jaw. He knows it's his most attractive feature. He knows Kartik finds him attractive. Kartik can tell, from the tilt of his neck, from the slow movement of his gaze.

Bidar, he replies. Silver, with an antique look.

A man shuffles out from behind a curtain that leads to the back of the shop. He has a small white beard and wizened coffee skin. He nods at Kartik, then says, adjusting his skullcap, I'm off to pray, Shahrukh.

The man's departure seems to unknot Shahrukh. His shoulders relax under his brown kurta; his face opens like the door of a cage. My parents met at a Shahrukh Khan film, he volunteers. Ammi was selling tickets, and Abbu was buying.

He stands and opens the display rack. His hand darts with practiced ease. He extracts six bangles. They release six sonorous clinks as he places them on the glass counter.

Which one? Kartik asks him. You pick.

Shahrukh sits down and leans forward. Kartik smells the perfume on his neck. A scent full of smoke and wood. His left cheek is scarred somewhat; the tip of his tongue gleams against one side of his mouth. They hear the azaan. The singer's voice is husky. Shahrukh points to the bangle third from the right.

You didn't even look, Kartik protests.

I knew, Shahrukh tells him, when I pulled it off the shelf.

He places the bangle in an envelope like it's a letter.

Kartik pays, takes the envelope, and asks Shahrukh out to dinner. He suggests Shadab. It's nearby but not fancy, he acknowledges.

It's unique, Shahrukh says. Two men going to Shadab on their first date? Janab. We'll make history in the city's oldest biriyani joint.

He reaches under the counter. An object flashes between his fingers. He slips it into his trouser pocket.

Shahrukh points to the Lakshmi temple abutting one of the Charminar's minarets. He says, The first Nizam king propitiated the goddess. When she showed up, pleased with his devotion, he tricked her into staying.

How? Kartik asks. He knows the story, but he wants to hear it again.

Shahrukh replies, He tells the goddess he's got an urgent errand to finish. Before leaving, he extracts from her a promise that she won't leave until he returns. And he never returns. The goddess knows, of course. She finds the ruse clever and blesses the Nizams with wealth that sees them through the rise and fall of the Mughal and British empires.

They take a corner table at Shadab. On the opposite wall is a framed quote from the Quran, white Arabic letters sewn into a green cloth. The place is crowded with the men who were at Jama Masjid. They're immersed in food and conversation. The air is thick with the scents of hot spices and cardamom. A qawwali plays on the speaker, the poet Ghalib's words punctuated with rhythmic, forceful claps: *Allow me, Imam, to drink in the mosque or show me to a corner where God isn't there.*

After the waiter serves them their food and takes their money, Shahrukh picks up the envelope from the table and extracts the bangle. He takes Kartik's hand and slips the bangle down his wrist. Shahrukh's teeth gleam in Shadab's orange glow. It feels to Kartik like magic, affection expressed in the open.

Do you want to meet Samosa? Shahrukh asks.

I'd like to eat one, Kartik says.

Samosa is my dog, Shahrukh says and laughs.

They eat from the same steaming plate of biriyani with their hands. They imbibe sweet tea from the same hot steel cup they pass back and forth. It's a place of communal eating. No one blinks an eye at them.

They lie next to each other on the hotel bed, fully clothed.

What are you doing in Hyderabad? Shahrukh asks.

I'm *from* Hyderabad, Kartik replies.

He recounts the incident: he in the kitchen, refilling his glass with water; a notification sounds from his phone, left on the dinner table unlocked; he's out in a flash, the tap left running; his phone in his father's hand; on the screen, the dating app: a private message and a picture attachment; his mother sees it next and grips her head; she cries; his father stands, returns his phone, and strikes him across the face before sitting down; he says, I'm giving you a year to get this hobby out of your system. After that, you're getting married. Clear?

He called it a "hobby," Kartik says. In a year, prospective brides will sit in my drawing hall with their parents and ask me what I studied, where I work, how much I earn. I play tourist to forget that future.

Shahrukh turns and places his foot on Kartik's ankles. A wave of electricity shoots through Kartik's body.

Will you take your kurta off for me? he asks.

Shahrukh yanks his kurta off and tosses it to the floor without breaking contact.

I have an enchanted bangle, Shahrukh tells him. Its magic is real.

He taps his trouser pocket.

Kartik runs his fingers through the hair on Shahrukh's chest. He's heard what Shahrukh has said, but what's more magical than a beautiful man whom Kartik desires and who, like some miracle, desires him back?

This bangle, Shahrukh continues, is made of mirror. If you look into it and ask a question, it will give you the answer. If you ask a question about the future, you must do what the bangle shows. The djinn who controls the bangle's magic doesn't like being wrong.

Kartik laughs. He touches Shahrukh's jaw. Let's call it a night? he says.

Shahrukh mounts Kartik, and Kartik wraps his hands around Shahrukh's warm back.

Kartik befriends Samosa the next day by feeding her ice cream. One spoonful at a time. She has large brown eyes, a thick white tail, and caramel fur that glows in the sunlight. They bring her to Kartik's hotel. The manager, Su, doesn't object. She knows Samosa. And she *knows*. Her eyes shine as she watches Shahrukh and Kartik as they wait for the elevator, their shoulders touching.

Kartik points to the GRE workbook Shahrukh holds.

I want to do my Masters in New York, Shahrukh says. Right now the book is a ruse. Abbu thinks I'm studying with Zaid, who, incidentally, thinks I'm on a Tinder date.

Kartik aches for that future: a room in Brooklyn with Shahrukh. Kartik's parents moved in with him as soon as he started working. If he had objected, his family would have branded him an ungrateful wretch for not caring for his aging parents. The real problem, Kartik knows, is that he's internalized their way of thinking.

Samosa naps on the balcony. Shahrukh sits on a chair next to her and spreads his legs. Kartik sits between his thighs. Shahrukh takes out the magic bangle. It reflects the Charminar behind them. They stick to safe questions.

Whom am I falling in love with? Kartik asks.

The reflected reality doesn't fade. But soon Shahrukh's face appears over it: first as an outline, then fully pronounced. It is a snapshot from last evening, when Kartik saw him through the lens of his camera.

Creep, Shahrukh teases. He asks the bangle the same question, and Kartik's face from the restaurant appears.

The answers are broader than the question. Now they each know the point at which the other fell for him.

A fakir gave it to me at an Eid fair, Shahrukh says.

He had a crush on you, Kartik says with a grave nod.

Stop, Shahrukh says, laughing. I was *eighteen.* The fakir looked like he hadn't seen a shower in some time, but his shawl smelled of new cotton. I bought him a plate of biriyani—he said he was hungry. He took out this bangle, looked into it, and murmured in a language I didn't understand. He smiled after a moment. A bangle for the bangle seller's boy, he said, holding it out. He told me it was magic. You're the first person I've showed it to.

You met him again? Kartik asks.

Shahrukh's answer confirms what he already knows.

They walk to Shadab for biriyani and chai, Samosa in tow.

What if your parents show up here? Shahrukh asks.

They won't, says Kartik.

Shahrukh looks at the bangle. Do Kartik's parents like Muslims? he asks.

Kartik apologizes for the bangle's answer.

We can't apologize for our parents, Shahrukh says, his smile sad.

Kartik wakes in the night, cold. Shahrukh is asleep with his hand wrapped around Samosa. The dog softly snores. Shahrukh's black hair shivers in the breeze of the fan. The room is drenched in moonlight. Kartik gets up and puts on a T-shirt and pajamas. He notices the bangle on the bedside table. He picks it up and addresses the djinn.

I bet you are as powerful as Aladdin's djinn. Who are you anyway? he asks.

After a moment, he puts down the bangle and climbs into bed, covering Shahrukh, Samosa, and himself with a blanket.

Who is he, the djinn? Shahrukh asks, his eyes still closed.

Not he, Kartik says. *She.* She lives in a minaret in the middle of a desert. The Thar, I'm guessing, from her outfit. A choli-lehenga. She plays a sarod and has a pet camel.

Shahrukh says, Our mullah said that if you use djinn magic to get what you want, a hundred different things will have to realign to make the new reality happen. You'll lose a lot in the process. It's the price you pay for defying fate.

His eyes open. His irises, emerald by day, are moss by moonlight.

Am I worth that price? Shahrukh asks. You don't even know me.

I know I like you, Kartik replies. And you're a man. That's better than marrying a girl of my parents' choosing. There's a price to pay either way.

Under the blanket, Shahrukh places his foot on Kartik's ankles.

On Monday they stand on the balcony and watch people on the street smear one another's necks and faces with color and water. The sectarian difference, made particularly volatile under the current regime, vanishes. The only riot is that of colors staining the air pink, blue, and green. The only guns fired are water guns. The only shrieks are those that rise from throats drunk on bhang: milk steeped with cannabis, ginger, cardamom, and rose and served cold. Kartik and Shahrukh don't partake in the festivities. They want to spend their last day together exclusively in each other's company. Su has brought them a jug of bhang. They take turns drinking from it directly.

They sit with their backs to the balcony wall. Shahrukh holds the jug away from Samosa, who's eager for a lick. Kartik tells Shahrukh a story. Two boys fell in love a long time ago, but they knew their elders wouldn't let them get married, so they fled to the forest and hung themselves from the oldest tree. But the tree spirit, moved by their love, reincarnated them as plants. Tobacco and cannabis. Lovers bound forever in a wedlock of intoxication.

Shahrukh smiles and leans forward and claims the white liquor mustache on Kartik's upper lip.

The next morning the light from Jama Masjid radiates a glow where dawn has colored the sky blue. Kartik books an Uber, and

Shahrukh packs his bag. Samosa stands up, shakes herself, and stares at Kartik.

She knows, Shahrukh says, zipping the bag. He leaves it by the door.

They lie next to each other on the bed, their fingers laced. Samosa lies next to Kartik, her paw on his chest. When Kartik's phone beeps, informing them the car is three minutes away, they sit up. Kartik kneels on the floor and slips Shahrukh's sandals onto his feet. Shahrukh slips Kartik's bangle down his wrist. It feels like a wedding.

They walk to the balcony. Shahrukh holds out the magic bangle.

Kartik poses the question that's on both their minds.

They wait, and from the corner of his eye, Kartik sees the car cruising down the street. It stops in front of the hotel. Samosa woofs. The light from the mosque gleams on the face of the bangle. The sound of the future fills Kartik's chest. A clap sounded twice.

MARY ANGELINO

Dear Girlhood

1. Anagrams for girls who don't play in the sea

My sleepyhead—all heeltaps
and leash, all pleated
and petaled from playdates—

ahead are steeples
of sea, pedestals of atlas
elapsing. Don't let girlhood

drift, don't dare it to drag—
my eyelash, my sad little eel.
So what? I'll deal.
I'm gloried, adored, she sings, haloed

and splayed on the shore. (I'm all plea,
no play.) Death an eyeshade,
a pale lady, wades into the deep.

2. *Song for queer girls*

For catching pollywogs (those squirmy
commas) with a net or hands or any
chipped wayward old mug; for mud-caked
Barbie's hair, for the cleft of plastic

(like a comma, net, or hands)
between her legs, for her shiny
hair and her clefts of plastic
breasts and for Velcro's easy rip-away

between her legs; for my shiny,
wooly strokes. For loving the neighbor girl's
breasts and for Velcro's easy rip-away
when I loved myself, for my pillow's

wooly strokes. For loving the neighbor girl
and her mother's, *Be back when the streetlights
come on*. For loving myself, my pillow,
and all the girls who stayed out past dark,

after the streetlights came on, their voices
chipped wayward old mugs. For mud-caked
girls who stayed out past dark.
For Barbie's hair. For the cleft of plastic.

3. How girls are made

She's old enough to wonder how it's done.
Her thumbs slide across the screen
and those little comet tails between the letters
trail, they clip *made* down to *mad* and *dam* and *me*,
or stretch it to *demons* or *demand*—see how
maiden weaves herself in? Sometimes
a cheerful *mead*, a willful *dame*.

A willful dame, a cheerful mead—
sometimes a maiden weaves herself in.
See how it stretches to demons or demand,
how dam and mad clips down to me?
Between the letters, those little comet tails
slide across the screen; her thumbs
wonder how it's done. She's old enough.

4. How the girl got thick skin

First, she felt it thin and shrink
like a child caught in a lie,
so she took it off and carried it.
Please don't ask how she looked

underneath (like a child caught in a lie),
splashing through the creek.
Please don't ask how she looked
when she hid, when a predator—mid-hunt—

splashed through the creek. You want to
know how she stretched and toughened
that hide when the predator was through,
how it felt to slip back into her skin—

its arguments stretched and toughened,
outgrown. She took it off, carried it,
turned it back into skin, and slipped in.
Don't ask how she looked.

CLAYTON BRADSHAW

The Ungrateful Dead

The same summer the San Antonio Spurs defeat the Miami Heat in Game 5 of the NBA Finals, Robin Williams hangs himself in his final act of ironic comedy, the Philae lander tumbles towards its fateful rendezvous with the Churyumov-Gerasimenko comet, and an overheated Eric Garner dies breathless in a chokehold, Grayce stands before the judge in Homerville, Georgia, and declares: Greg Clarkson is dead. I killed him.

Three months earlier, Grayce stops a millimeter past the stop sign when a cop pulls them over. The red-and-blue lights flash purple against the hood of their car, and they know better than to roll forward that last inch, but they're in a hurry. They aren't exactly late for their Saturday shift at Sonic, but every cell in their brain has been shifting in twelve different directions as though they are. In fact, they've been in such a rush, they've forgotten their driver's license.

The cop walks up to the side of Grayce's window and knocks on the salt-coated glass. Grayce rolls down the window and notices their reflection in the cop's boots and immediately adjusts their glasses. When they tell the officer their license is at home, the cop asks, Well, do you know the number? I'll just run it through the computer. Grayce recites from memory what they believe the number to be, which turns out to be the number for a license belonging to someone named Greg Clarkson. When the cop returns, his lips are twisted towards the right side of his face.

At the jail, Grayce stands against a wall, their back rigid against the white-painted cinderblocks. An older white woman in a gray uniform pressed tightly against her body armor grabs Grayce by the wrist and drags them to a cold steel table under a dark-lensed camera. Grayce shrieks.

Hey, that fucking hurts, they say.

The woman points to a sign on the wall above the table. *No foul language*, the sign says. She firmly grasps Grayce's index finger and rolls it back and forth onto a cold inkpad. Then she rolls the finger on a thin, blue piece of cardstock with faint black grids printed on one side. She repeats this process with each finger on Grayce's left hand. Then again with each finger on Grayce's right hand. The woman seems invested in the efficiency of the procedure and does not speak to Grayce.

As their fingers press against the cardstock, Grayce begins to feel enclosed by the room and the woman's grip on their fingers. Their breathing grows shallow and depthless, and the synapses in their brain spark bright and effulgent until Grayce collapses onto the floor. The woman takes Grayce's limp hand and presses their right pinkie onto the ink and then the cardstock.

In a hospital, Grayce wakes up, their hands cuffed to the bed. They recognize the smoky image of Greg in the corner of the room, like a gaseous space cloud, his hands opened wide and reaching towards Grayce's neck. Grayce breathes harder and harder, and Greg fades in and out of translucence as he inches his way towards Grayce in a fantastically spectral fashion. Grayce grips the sides of the hospital bed. A nurse administers a sedative and Grayce's spine relaxes, their head sinking into the pillow. The world slows into shrinking ambiguity.

Grayce's body feels numb, pliant and compliant, as they sit in the back of the police car on the way back to the jail. They slump into the seat, their head placed against the plate glass of the side window. The officer stares straight down the road ahead, never acknowledging Grayce's presence, as though he's forgotten Grayce exists within the space of his patrol car. Grayce feels strangely comfortable; they are not used to this degree of obscurity.

Walking through the heavy steel doors of the jail, an officer they've never seen before steers Grayce with a firm hand on their shoulder. In the cell, a dishwater-colored mattress sits rolled up on a stainless-steel bed bolted to the wall. The officer tosses into the cell a faded black-and-white striped shirt and pair of pants that smell of laundry detergent, though they look as though they have never been cleaned.

Those should fit, the officer says.

On the edge of their cold steel bed, Grayce sits, staring at the bricks, and the numbness begins to fade. They feel their mind easing into a nice Sunday-morning pace as another officer they've never seen before opens the plexiglass door. He claps his hands together twice.

Get up, he says.

Grayce blinks, acutely conscious of the corner of the bed poking into their leg.

Greg is dead, they blurt out.

The officer blinks, and Grayce feels their head pulsate as the gravity of their situation becomes weightless and the blood rises into their brain.

The officer balls his fist. We'll get a confession later, he says. Get moving. You're going to the men's tank.

Grayce doesn't want to confess, at least not without a lawyer present. They learned this by watching *Law and Order*. Cops never have your best interest in mind, they will later tell their mother. They just want to assert authority over who they think you are. Grayce has only ever seen one episode, but they feel very confident in their assessment. At any rate, they tell the officer they cannot go to the men's tank because they are neither a man nor a fish.

The officer leaves, then returns with a can that looks like an air horn. Grayce stares into the orange cone nozzle. They cover their ears, but there is no sound. Only a spicy, peppery, piquant pain. They fall to the ground and rub the mace deeper into their eyes. Their nerves shriek again. Grayce washes their face for two hours, not realizing this only spreads the oil and capsicum and generally makes matters worse. They certainly never think to splash their eyes with milk from the carton on the tray of food left behind for them. When the burning finally begins to fade, the officer returns to point the mace at them one more time. Grayce collapses inward into numbness again.

In the men's tank, the other inmates look at Grayce with what Grayce believes is caution. Grayce unrolls their bedsheets and makes their bed in the corner closest to the door. An older man whose glasses barely fit over his long, white hair and beard says, I don't think you belong in this cell.

That's because I don't, Grayce says.

To be fair, none of us do, the man says, but we don't have much choice, I suppose. He walks back to his bunk and pulls out a package of ramen from under his bed. I know you haven't gotten a chance to order anything from the commissary, and I imagine you aren't used to eating breakfast at four in the morning. Just get one for me when you get a chance.

Grayce has no clue what the old man is talking about, but they accept the package of ramen. A younger man with a shaved head paces near the toilet at the back of the cell. He stops to look at Grayce, then continues his pacing. Later, Grayce learns the young man is named Billy. He'd run over a parking meter outside the courthouse for the third time and couldn't pay the fines he'd incurred.

Grayce heats some water from the sink with the coffee maker next to the old man's bunk. While they wait for the water to soak into the ramen, they brush their teeth with the miniature toothpaste and brush that was given to them in a Ziplock bag. In the mirror, they see only Greg and lose their appetite and give the ramen to Billy so he'll stop pacing.

Later that afternoon, Grayce is brought to another cell where a detective in an unbuttoned gray suit jacket and brown tie waits. He stands in the corner with his arms crossed like a cop from a TV show. Grayce sits in a red plastic chair that has been brought in from the processing area. Where is Greg's body? the detective asks. We know you did something with it. Grayce imagines the detective has a New York accent because, in their mind, all detectives are from New York.

Somewhere inside me, Grayce says. I feel I can never get rid of him.

You fucking ate Greg? The detective's cuff shoots from his suit as he straightens his arm.

Grayce looks down at the cement floor. I mean I swallowed him deep inside me.

The detective softly pounds his fist against the wall. He looks to the ceiling, eyes lifted as though he is asking God for permission to beat Grayce into compliance. You're going to have to be a touch clearer. Is any part of Greg's body buried somewhere we can find it? Or did you eat everything, bones and all?

Grayce giggles, shakes their head, and giggles some more, unable to excavate the vocabulary they need. He is certainly buried, they say.

Oh, you sick bastard. The detective's eyebrows twist towards one another.

Grayce sees Greg in the stainless-steel mirror behind the man. They recognize the thin eyebrows and the weather-beaten grimace. They've tried so hard to forget him. Grayce shouts and points to the mirror, lets the detective know Greg is there with them even if he isn't really, but they can't fully form the words before the detective storms out of the cell.

Greg emerges from the mirror. You miss me, don't you? he says. You miss how your mom used to look at you when I inhabited your body. You miss how I only shaved when the stubble began to scratch and how you weren't so anxious when the teacher assigned you a desk in the first row of the classroom because you weren't worried anyone would make fun of you. I took care of you, Greg says.

Grayce shakes their head, then stops. They say, There were moments when you made my life easier, but I didn't like that you did.

Back in their cell in the men's tank, Grayce lies on the unrolled mat on their bed. They sob uncontrollably. Billy yells across the room, Shut up before I come make you, which only makes Grayce sob harder. The old man, Grimes, Grayce thinks he calls himself, throws a legal pad at Billy and tells him he is the one who needs to shut up. Grayce pauses her sobbing, thankful for the kindness, before deciding they can fight their own battles. They tighten their shoulders, cross the room, and sock Billy with the pillow from their bed. Don't fucking tell me to shut up, asshole, Greg says through Grayce. Billy seems stunned and sits on the floor and commences his own sobbing.

At their bunk, Grayce purges themself of Greg by running a comb from the toiletries bag through their hair to smooth out the tangles it has accumulated through the day. Grimes directs a thumbs up at Grayce and tells them they will survive prison just fine if and when they are transferred there. Grayce shakes their head and whispers to themself that they are not Greg and that Greg no longer has authority over their body and cannot be allowed to possess them like that anymore.

In the magistrate's office, Grayce stands between a man and a woman, each in the same semi-laundered uniform as Grayce. The magistrate addresses the man first. Lenny Kyle, you are charged with armed robbery and assault with a deadly weapon. Do you understand these charges?

Yes, ma'am, Lenny says.

I am setting your bail for $1,500. Officer Thompson, hand this paperwork to Mr. Kyle to sign. The magistrate continues. Sarah Baldwin, you are charged with driving while intoxicated. Do you understand the charge?

Yes, ma'am, Sarah says.

This is not your first offense. I am setting bail at $2,500. Officer Thompson, hand this paperwork to Mrs. Baldwin to sign. The magistrate turns to Grayce. You are charged with first-degree murder. Though you are seventeen, the serious nature of this crime means you will be tried as an adult. Do you understand?

Grayce breathes heavily and their head becomes frictionless. The magistrate's desk twists away from them.

Do you understand the charge? the magistrate repeats.

Grayce faints again, and the bailiff signs the paperwork for them.

A new inmate joins Grayce and Billy and Grimes in their cell. His name is John and he has been arrested for domestic violence. It was just an argument with his wife, he claims, but his skin is damp and his knuckles are bloody. Grayce offers him some ramen and says they won't judge him though they've already decided to steal Grimes's sharpened pencil and keep it under their pillow in case John tries something.

A man in a brown suit stands with his hands in his pockets in the corner of the conference room Grayce has been taken to. He points to a stapled stack of papers and sets a pen on top of the pile.

Here, sign this, he says.

Grayce looks over the paperwork, but the words feel equally concrete and abstract, the symbols familiar, the language incomprehensible, just large blocks of letters heaped atop one another in tightly-formed rectangles. What is it? they ask.

Your confession. At least the parts we can figure out. But don't you worry. We'll find Greg's body. We'll find it, all right.

Grayce can hear the Southern drawl in the lawyer's voice. Like *Matlock*, they think, if Matlock was a dick. But Greg doesn't have a body, Grayce says. He's dead.

Greg's ghost smiles at Grayce through the whites of the man's eyes. But am I? Grayce doesn't know if the man says this, or if Greg is speaking through him, or if Grayce has fabricated the whole thing. They roll their eyes and say they won't sign something that isn't true. They didn't murder Greg; they just ended his life.

The man in the gray suit looks stunned at the non-confession and leans back in his chair until the front legs lift off the floor. There's a moment when he looks as though he might fall backwards. We don't need you to sign anything, but you'll have to enter a plea tomorrow. Plead guilty and I'll recommend leniency. He packs up his briefcase and walks out of the room.

Grayce waits for someone, anyone, to take them back to their cell.

That night, John shakes Grayce awake and says, I don't know what you are, but I'm horny enough not to care. Grayce pulls Grimes's pencil from under their pillow and stabs John in the shoulder with it. Grimes presses the button to call the guards, who separate Grayce and John.

Both Grimes and Billy testify that Grayce stabbed John in self-defense and that John should be removed from their cell so no one else is put in danger, but the guards roll up Grayce's mattress with the sheets still laid out over it and stuff Grayce's extra pair of underwear in a bag with their toiletries and move them to a cell on the other side of the hallway. An hour before breakfast, Grayce wakes up and looks through the plexiglass window and sees John staring at them with a hand down his pants. Grayce calls the guards, but the guards only tell them to go back to sleep.

Grayce wraps themself up in their bedding, but they cannot fall asleep. The sour air coming through the steel vent on the high ceiling smells like John's breath on their neck, and they can still feel his eyes from across two plates of plexiglass. They stare into the darkness, anticipating the biscuit made with too much flour they get for breakfast on Tuesdays. Greg's voice echoes in their mind. This will all be easier if you let me handle everything, he says.

No, Grayce whispers.

The next day, as Grayce waits to see the judge, they sit in the solitary cell with the pale wisps of Greg's ghost. He's quickly fading, his molecules dissolving, but what's left of his face warps into a familiar snarl. They're going to send you away for a long time, he tells Grayce. You tried killing me, but remember, you just buried me someplace deep.

Something, a brief rebellion or a moment of sass, stirs in Grayce. They bang on the plexiglass and scream as loud as they can, Guard, I can tell you where Greg is!

The guard nods quietly and walks towards the processing area.

When the government lawyer arrives at their cell, Grayce points to where the faded remnants of Greg's ghost had been sitting. The lawyer's eyeballs jut past his eyelids; his eyebrows point inward. There's nothing there, he says. His knees bend ninety degrees as he lets his back fall onto the wall. I don't get you, his eyes seem to repeat over and over.

Grayce looks again in Greg's direction and sees only themself in the dull reflection of the steel sink. The lawyer leaves, and Grayce sits on the cold bed and exhales any incorporeal exhaust that might remain of Greg's presence. When the breath returns to their body, they ask, Are you gone?

The stale air flows through the cell.

There is no response.

Later, when the judge asks Grayce for their plea, Grayce feels as though their stomach has been stuffed with gossamer and then instantly emptied. The world of the story forced upon Grayce fades and is replaced by one of their own design. They straighten their back, look the judge in the eye, and state firmly and clearly, Greg Clarkson is dead. I killed him. But, Grayce continues, he never truly existed in the first place.

But your plea, the judge prods.

Not guilty, your honor. You can't kill someone who was never really here.

And for weeks and months and years beyond this moment, Grayce Clarkson will state their case through the glossed walnut lens of the witness stand, exasperated, never quite able to convince the government lawyer with his Georgia accent and his brown corduroy suit that Greg once held their life hostage and his death was an act of self-defense.

ROBERT CARR

At the Hatter's Table

Edible. Sometimes. Cool
Whip, dream whip, buttercream,

butter stick, sweet and sour, fruit
spread, cocoa on my junk.

I think of myself as cake:
A flesh-colored icing, a grand-

daddy banquet at the Hatter's table.
Ageless set of creases, a multi-

layered thing, so happy to be split.
Serve me on a platter washed in tears,

in sweat, in any other viscous liquid.
Write my name, and yours,

on an iced pink chest,
encircle us with a heart, squeeze

what you desire from your tube of batter.

ANNA GRAEME

sphinx women

Sphinx women find jobs on the street
as women who sell fruit and bright clothes
and handmade jewelry. They smile with sharp teeth.
They have angry, lovely eyes that burn like
dark honey. They cover their breasts now
and keep their paws hidden under heavy skirts
and shawls. Handsewn and bleeding through
ages of bronze, of analog clocks. They keep riddles
and wisdoms off their tongues. It would all be drowned
out anyway. Always with the steel and the sound of the rail,
charging like the Cretan Bull, beneath them.
Sphinx women pay child support ten times over
for lion cubs already gone. They talk under brick
ledges in city rain, in hushed barbed tongues. No,
years of kings and heroes weren't much better. But
at least there had been warm blood
and good, wild words to give.

HANNAH GRIECO

If you were red riding hood

and I found you, sniffed you out on the path with your basket, your cape, your soft hair, your pink-orange freckles lit by the sun piercing the canopy, and if I jumped out, held up my thick paws and clipped nails, opened my mouth wide, to show not teeth but hunger, not teeth but patience, as you walked this forest over and over, as I smelled the wishes rising from your skin, smelled the jail smell of your life, of this routine of caregiving, of caring, of giving, and if I searched and found the red haloing your head, the fire of everything you wanted to be, everything your mother and grandmother and great-grandmother wanted you to be, if you cried out, but it wasn't fear, and then touched me, traced the pads of my palms, and said *what big hands you have*, said *you're so hungry*, said *I used to fear this path*, then I could finally tell you *I'm not really a wolf*, and you'd run your fingers up my arms, dig the tips down through the fur to my skin, and say *girls can be wolves too*, if you reached up to my lips, pushing your hands into my mouth, if you said *take me someplace new* as I tried to whisper around you, my mouth full, as I tried to tell you *let the ax man come, I'll slice myself open*, you'd hush me, widen my mouth, push in up to your elbows, crawl all the way inside, and I'd turn and run the both of us from these woods.

ALLEGRA HYDE

A Whale Tale

The whale was already dead when it washed ashore. A massive sperm whale, its skin leathery and barnacled, its narrow jaw strutted with teeth. The whole town went down to the beach to see it: mothers and firefighters and stay-at-home dads and dead-beat dads and vacuum cleaner salespeople and endometriologists and dowagers and women of the night and diamond miners and fortune tellers and personal trainers. Children were bussed in from school. Prisoners from prison. Altogether, the townspeople encircled the creature, reaching forward to touch its gray-blue skin. People wept. People waved flags. People complained about not being able to barbecue because of health ordinances.

More than anything, people wondered how the whale had died.

A coroner-for-whales was summoned to conduct an autopsy. She began to cut the whale open right there on the beach, excavating through layers of blubber. Because it had taken her so long to arrive, however, and because it had started drizzling—and also because the work was gruesome—almost everyone went home before the procedure was complete. Everyone except for a few diehard protesters, local news reporters, police officers, orphans, and a man named Anders.

Anders did not usually attend public spectacles such as this. He had merely been driving by on his way home from his job at a nonprofit for bicycle safety. He had ventured onto the beach because of the crowds and had stayed because of the whale.

Or, more truthfully: Anders had stayed because it meant he could delay going home. And if he delayed going home, then he could delay returning to his longtime lover, Florian. And if he delayed returning to Florian, he could delay doing what he had promised himself he would do—which was end their relationship.

The coroner-for-whales went about her work. She used a special saw to cut into the creature's vast flank. She was aiming for its stomach, she told onlookers. She was getting close. Like everyone in the crowd,

Anders drew an anticipatory breath, though the sight of the whale disturbed him. Fins motionless. Glassy eyes staring at nothing. The bigness of the animal—the deadness of it, too—put a stone in his gut. Hard and round and heavy, the stone gave Anders the sinking sensation of foreboding.

Or else: the foreboding came from what he planned to do when he got home.

Anders loved Florian—or *had* loved him, early on in their seven-year relationship. Florian, who was all sparkles and beauty. Florian, with his sandy hair and sea-glass eyes. Florian, who was the son of a local witch/naturopath, who could whistle like the wind singing through trees, and who had at one time taken Anders's breath away, but now took all of Anders's money and time and energy, and who refused to get a job.

"And we're in!" The coroner tossed her saw aside and extended a gloved arm into the cavernous opening of the whale's stomach.

Anders felt the stone in his gut grow heavier. He had no business watching this creature be disemboweled. But his relationship with Florian was over—needed to be over—and he couldn't yet bear to admit this to Florian's face. So he pushed through the crowd to see what made the others yelp with surprise.

The whale's stomach was bursting with stuff. *Human* stuff. A wide-screen television. A wooden bed frame. Woolen socks, both matched and unmatched. Plastic fruit. A two-slice toaster. Several doilies—or so Anders guessed. Some items were hard to identify, covered as they were with the whale's stomach slime.

Next came a corduroy-upholstered couch. A set of collectible spoons from Midwest states. A rolltop desk. A pair of roller skates—which made Anders lean closer, since the skates were similar to a pair he'd just purchased. The couch, too, reminded him of the couch he owned, which he'd believed to be one of a kind.

People grabbed items, inspected them, expressed their dismay and confusion. A reporter waved aloft a photo frame containing a picture of two people—shouted that he had found a clue—that is, until his eyes fell on Anders. The reporter looked back at the frame. At Anders. At the frame. At Anders.

"It's you," said the reporter.

"What?" said Anders.

"This is you in this picture." The reporter shoved the frame under Anders's nose.

The photo was of Anders and Florian. It was from a day at the beach, actually. A selfie they'd taken right before moving in together. The framed photo sat on their mantel at home.

"I don't know how that got in there," said Anders. "That can't be . . ."

Others gathered around, looked back and forth from the framed selfie to Anders. Someone made the sign of the cross. Someone waved a fistful of collectible spoons in Anders's face, said, "Are these yours, too?"

Anders wasn't sure how to respond. He did own collectible spoons; he and Florian bought them whenever they went on road trips. They also owned a corduroy-upholstered couch. And roller skates. And doilies. And a widescreen TV. But how could these items have gotten inside the whale?

"Do all of these items belong to you?" asked the coroner-for-whales, pointedly.

The stone in Anders's belly grew even heavier.

"Yes," he confessed, backing away from the crowd. "But also no. This is impossible. I live miles inland and . . . I was home this morning . . . I . . ."

"You killed this whale," said a protester. "You *monster*."

Several of the orphans cowered in fear.

A policeperson vomited.

The reporters scribbled furiously.

The coroner-for-whales nodded with solemn disgust, made a note on her clipboard.

Later, after the official investigation had concluded and justice was deliberated upon, it was decided that Anders should be cut open—for scientific purposes. This would help determine what kind of sociopath fed his belongings to a whale.

In the months before the procedure, the townspeople speculated what they would find in Anders's stomach. Some guessed they'd find the remnants of lavish steak dinners. Others predicted seaweed and krill. Still others said bits of broken glass. Or prescription medications. Or a plume of grim, noxious smoke. Or an anchor. Or a message in a bottle. Or a baby whale.

Everyone had a theory and few theories aligned. What everyone agreed on, though, was that information illuminating the death of the whale was sure to be found inside Anders. Because Anders had seemed normal from the outside. He had even seemed pleasant: a taxpaying citizen who was neatly dressed and well-deodorized. But he denied having anything to do with the whale's death—and, clearly, that wasn't true.

"It *is* true," Anders muttered to himself while he waited for the procedure in the local prison tower. "I never saw that whale in my life."

He muttered many things, his mind frayed from months of solitary confinement. In the early days of his imprisonment, he had ranted—his voice echoing off the tower walls—angry at the townspeople, at the whale, at Florian. But, as time passed, his anger melted into bewilderment. Where was Florian, anyway? He hadn't been at the trial, hadn't ever come to visit Anders. Was it possible Florian had been the one to toss all their household items into the sea after getting wind of Anders's plans to end their relationship? Unlikely, since Florian wasn't prone to emotional outbursts and didn't care for physical labor. Sometimes, Anders wondered if he *himself* had done the tossing, perhaps in a fugue state. But this, too, was unlikely. Anders knew himself to be a man of discipline and focus.

Or else, he *had* been, except when it came to Florian.

As the days ticked closer to his scheduled procedure, Anders drifted from bewilderment to nostalgia. He wished he could hold Florian. He wished he could listen to Florian whistle. He wished he could brush Florian's sandy hair from his delicate face. So what if Florian slept in, lazed about, and demonstrated no discernable goals or ambitions?

Alone in the prison tower, Anders remembered how, when he and Florian were first courting, they'd spent hours walking up and down the beach. Anders had been the pursuer then. He had noticed Florian at a local fish fry and was smitten by the younger man's shimmering beauty. Everyone knew it was risky to get involved with the son of a witch, but when Anders imagined life with Florian, he imagined having access to a constant source of wonderment and joy.

Come home with me, Anders had said to Florian as they walked the beach one evening. The pair had known each other only a few weeks, but the moment felt right: the sky blushing pink, the ocean spreading smooth as a mirror all the way to the horizon. *Come home with me,* Anders repeated. *I'll take care of you. I'll love you forever.*

Florian had studied Anders, uncertain. For all his playfulness and grace—his fortitude as a whistler—Florian could be skittish at times. Shy, even.

You have to mean it, he told Anders.

Anders had never been one for gallant gestures, for ceremony either. He believed in safety protocol, punctuality, and staying in his lane. But being around Florian made him want to live in a grander fashion: to have feelings and experiences that were leviathan-large. And so Anders bent down and selected a smooth flat stone from the sand. He pressed the stone to his lips, then flung it toward the sea so that it skipped across the water, each bounce like the rise and fall of an invisible needle: a stitch that sutured up his words—bound them tight—before the stone was swallowed by the sea.

After that, Florian had agreed to come live with him.

Because he'd made a promise, Anders realized too late. Because he'd made a vow. *I'll take care of you. I'll love you forever.*

Anders had gotten involved with the son of a witch—how could he have expected to get uninvolved so easily? He should have known better. A man like him, especially: ever diligent and devoted to the rules.

What had the rules been in this case?

A promise made should remain a promise kept.

When Anders was at last cut open, the whole town gathered to watch. Mothers and casino owners and botanists and professional soccer players and podiatrists crowded into the operating chamber's viewing gallery and into overflow rooms equipped with a live video feed. People sold popcorn. People made bets. People had to be carted away for drunk and disorderly behavior.

A hush fell when Anders was wheeled into the operating chamber on a gurney. His torso was bare, his face blank from sedation. The townspeople held their breaths as the procedure commenced, everyone eager to resolve the mystery of the whale's death and Anders's role therein. And maybe it was this heightened buildup that left the townspeople so disappointed once the procedure was complete. Because when they opened up Anders, what they discovered inside him made little sense.

Or else: what they discovered made little sense to everyone *except* a sandy-haired man standing alone at the edge of the gallery. Only he didn't throw his popcorn into the air, or boo loudly, or groan about money lost in a bet. Instead, he wiped a tear from his eye and set his delicate jaw. Because he'd been on that beach seven years ago with Anders and he knew what it meant to behold the consequence of a promise reversed. A vow undone.

Because when they opened up Anders, they pulled out a stone.

CATHERINE KIM

The Fox Marble

It's nothing so profound, reads
her message to me as I wait beneath the
mantle where her portrait stands, *merely the ghost
of my affections on your fingers, which you take inside
your mouth in remembrance of me. Capture this dream in a
marble, moonstruck in a kiss, and behold the creatures of the
earth and the memory of salt, which is my warmth forever
trapped in the teeth of your thumb, and do not mind
the empty sky, which is the surface of the marble
from inside it. Won't you wait for me my
thousand days of hunger for you?*

From the overlook, Yeou could see the stretch of the village below her, from the paddy fields by the base of the mountain to the bus terminal at its furthest reach. With a finger outstretched towards the vanishing point, she could trace the road as it split from the highway and flowed into the village, winding around the homes, the crop fields, the greenhouses, and the livestock pens, past the irrigation pond and up the slope towards her perch. She couldn't see the asphalt turn to gravel, or the gravel turn to dirt, as the path up the mountain was swallowed by the canopy near the terraced gravesites. The branch she had fashioned into a walking stick had snapped during her climb, and chestnut burrs clung to the fabric of her shoes and her pant legs. Above her, the daylight poured through the heated colors of the leaves that still clung to the trees surrounding the burial mound. The sun fled over the crown of the mountain, a white-hot nimbus illuminating the monument on its peak. The clouds bent the sky into a dome, as if sometime during her ascent the heavens had collapsed around the earth and shrunk it inside an orb, or as if Yeou herself had grown into a giant who still thought herself an ordinary girl, tall enough to behold the curvature that was the boundary between this world and all that lay beyond it. Having come here in the wake of her beloved Nabi's passing, with thoughts of her stuck in Yeou's throat, Yeou was not surprised by how the horizon circumscribed the sights around her, only by the way the limitations of the world had now become visible to the naked eye.

Yeou leaned against her father's burial mound so that her head lay on the soft earth and the wildflowers tickled the back of her neck. She shut her eyes to blot out the strange geometry. She felt the wind haunting her lips; she heard it move through the leaves. She felt the kiss of the butterfly's feet as it perched on her nose; she heard the *crunch* of the grass under her father's shoes as he stepped out from behind the mound. She felt the weight of his hand as he ran his fingers through her hair and the pollen displaced by the butterfly's wings as it flew away.

She had meant to come with a rake, she said, to pick up the leaves, and a bill hook to cut away the overgrowth that threatened to shroud the path up to the clearing. But she'd forgotten to pack the garden tools and the plastic bags and the basket with containers of grilled fish and green grapes and a bottle of plum wine inside it. Instead, she found herself climbing up the mountain with nothing but the holes in her memory. Now that she was here, Yeou might prick her fingers prying the burrs from her clothes, then pull the weeds that were choking the crown of her father's burial mound. It was the least she could do, having neglected him for so long. She leaned against her father, pressing her temple to his shoulder, and breathed in the smoke that fled from his lips. Through the holes in her memory, he said, she might remember another's memories in turn. Long ago, buckled into a window seat on a bus headed to Seoul, the promise of an elsewhere had filled him up like water does the ears when the head is submerged while his only regret tugged at the roof of his mouth like a fishhook.

In the summers of his childhood, Yeou's father would slip out the door of his aunt's house in the blue before dawn and follow the path that snaked through the center of the village to the rice paddies and the irrigation pond, where the asphalt turned to gravel. He would lie on his stomach at the bank of the pond, and with his eyes adjusted to the lowlight, he would watch the sleeping fish as the earliest of them began to rouse. Some days he would hunt for frogs; on others, he'd pluck the wildflowers that grew on the edges of the path as the sun returned their colors. These he would wrap with an errant stem and bring them to the hanok on the highest hill before the mountain, where he'd place them at the foot of the gate, before pounding on it with the flat of his fist. As soon as he heard the inner doors to the courtyard slide open and the gravel crunch under familiar footsteps, he'd scamper down the street to the brick house owned by the old widow, scattering the strays from their bowls in the yard. Crouched behind the porch bars, he'd watch the gates of the hanok swing open to reveal the girl he wished to kiss. She would pick up the wildflowers and shake them until the bugs fell out. Some days she'd sit on the steps and pluck the crowns from the stems, squeezing their colors over her palms; on others, she'd yell in his direction that she'd only kiss a prince. She'd grind the flowers under her shoe and slam the gate shut. Never did she take the flowers with her.

One day, in the middle of a white-hot summer that saw the pond drain to a puddle, he trapped a frog in his hands and rushed to the hanok atop the hill and called to the girl to let him inside, promising her a kiss from a prince. The girl did not come out. He kicked the gate, and the clamor drew the attention of the widow down the street, who called for him from her spot on the porch. This time the strays did not scamper out of sight as he approached; instead, they lapped at their bowls and brushed their sides against his shins.

The widow told him that the girl had left the village, having caused a commotion at her father's funeral, fleeing down the mountain to hide on the widow's porch until her mother came to drive her home. Her father had told the girl he'd always be with her, and the girl had thought that meant he would live forever. Even as they lowered him into the earth, she waited for him to hammer his fists against the inside of the casket and climb out of it to keep his promise to her. As the strays had licked the tears from her hands and she wiped her eyes with her wet knuckles for their indirect kiss, the girl writhed in her hatred of the village, with its deathly mountain and sunbaked farmers and croaking frogs, the endless bugs and the stink of manure, the chestnut burrs that clung and pricked her through the fabric of her clothing. She wished she could grow into a tree, like the one that shadowed her father now, only bigger, with a crown as tall as the mountain and a trunk thick enough to support its own weight. If she were a giant tree, she'd sweep away the houses with an errant branch and starve the rice paddies with her greedy roots and pop the burial mounds like pustules with her many limbs. Fathers didn't lie to trees the way they lied to little girls.

The girl promised never to return to the village until she grew into that giant tree or until her father dug himself out of his grave to fulfill his promise.

Hearing this, Yeou's father thought the girl terribly wise, having heard cautionary tales about promises involving magic trees. He felt a pit yawn in his chest wide enough to swallow the frog in his hand, which is what must have happened as he unlatched his fingers to find them empty. As he grew older, he spent less of the year with his aunt in the countryside and more with another aunt in Seoul. In the city, the only fish he saw were at the supermarket; the only frogs he saw were in cartoons. His aunt ran her hand through his hair when he plucked a flower from the hedge surrounding her apartment and cut his finger on a thorn, and dragged him around a corner when he pounded on the metal gate of a hanok that seemed a strange reflection of the hanok in the village. Soon he could hardly remember the girl's face, or the widow's, or the names the widow had given the strays. The more the details swirled down the holes in his memory, the more he thought he recognized the girl in the faces of girls who played on the playground in the apartment complex, or in the library where his aunt did her coursework, or in the subway car on his way to school, or in the courtyard of the girls' school down the street from his own. Every time Yeou's father thought he recognized the girl in the face of another, he would ask them if they knew of a girl from the countryside who lived in the shadow of a mountain filled with graves, near a pond overflowing with frogs and fish, a girl who was saving her first kiss for a prince, a girl who might resemble them from a distance, but none of them ever knew who she was.

One day, on an aimless walk through an unfamiliar district, he found a burial mound facing the street, with only the sidewalk and a guardrail separating it from the traffic, as if the gravesite had been plucked from the side of the mountain and transposed there. So peculiar was this sight that he didn't see the girl at first, alerted to her presence only by the *snap-click!* of her camera, which caught both him and the burial mound in the range of its fisheye lens. Turning to face her, he realized he must have stumbled through a slip in the veil to the other world, for what else could explain the strange placement of the burial mound and the girl who stood before him, ethereal in that suspended moment? He called her by her name, having just remembered it by the flower that fell from its perch behind the girl's ear, and expected her to respond with his own, only for the illusion to collapse as she lowered the camera to reveal her face. She told him he must have mistaken her for someone else.

This encounter lingered with him, but by the time he'd completed his military service and declared his major in literature, he had given up asking after the girl from the village, realizing he would never find her unless she became a giant tree, which would surely be visible from the windows of his new apartment or be covered on the news. It was during this period of disillusionment, in a class on Milton's *Paradise Lost*, as the professor wrote on the blackboard the passage wherein God sends Michael with a band of Cherubim to exile Adam and Eve, that a student who seemed to him very plain, whose face was so indistinctive he barely recognized her as his classmate, approached him and asked if he knew of a boy who spent his summers in a village by a mountain, plucking wildflowers and chasing frogs and frightening strays, who had promised her a kiss from a prince, and looked very much like him, though she could see now that he was right in front of her that he must be a stranger after all.

Now the world had inverted itself, Yeou's father told her, with him waiting by his own grave for his own child to visit him. Some days, as the daylight crested over the mountain, he thought he could see a flaming sword mounted on its peak, as well as the ghostly valley beyond it. The dusk painted the clouds in the colors of a burning bush, which in the sky appeared to be a giant tree, stretching over the glass in its long embrace. With her eyes still shut, Yeou thought all the butterflies must be at rest. She rubbed the bridge of her nose against her father's shoulder before settling her head in the crook of his neck.

As a child, he said, he'd been pulled by the hook in the roof of his mouth to the fish sleeping in the pond. He'd thought all the still and silent secrets of the world might be divined in the water, in the drift of the dreamers in its hold. He'd thought himself enlightened, having learned from a parable that in order to gain an understanding of earth and heaven, the student must steal the fox marble from the shapeshifter with a kiss and behold both the ground beneath him and the sky above him in the measure of that affection. In the blue of the early twilight, the water was a perfect reflection of the sky. If he had anything left to give his child, it was his wish that the hook in her mouth would lead her not to the surface of the water, but pull her out of the fox marble, for all the promises of earth and heaven could not dislodge the thing that was stuck in her throat and there was a world outside the orb of her grief.

And as Yeou opened her eyes to let in the light cresting the peak of the mountain, first her father's voice, then his burial mound, and at last the mountain itself fell beneath her. Or perhaps she had taken flight, reeled towards the surface of the marble by the fishhook, so that the sunset became the sunrise, with her suspended on the string of its shimmering heat. In that way, she saw the mountain collapse into itself, as if every grave on its face, having grown into deeper hollows, had demanded all at once that their hungers be sated and the very landscape was reshaped by the chorus of their desires. She saw the water in the pond sink beneath its own depths, leaving to dry its school of fish, rudely awakened and gasping for breath in the empty air. She saw the path that wound through the village contort into an ophidian shape, stretching the bounds of the rice paddies until they burst. She saw it crush the buildings in its coils until nothing was left but the village's wreckage, which crumbled into dust as it fell out of sight. Soon all that remained was the great expanse, which stretched towards the horizon, then over and beyond it, and finding the glass there, Yeou's vision pressed against the curve until the orb unfurled into a white sheet to reveal even more of its endlessness.

Yeou had dreamed all her life of changing her shape. Back when she was a child, she had planted her feet in the dirt and stretched her arms up towards the sky so that her bones might reshape her into a woman grown. She had licked at her teeth every night, to lap away the taste of mint and to hone them into points, so that when she bit into her father's wrist, she might be a fox sinking her canines into bone and not a child crying from the silver caps on her molars, having failed to penetrate his skin. So she learned how to change her shape from her mother, who had wanted to be a mother and a wife and had become both a woman and a tree so that her husband might perch on a branch and sing to her the names of all the birds in the sky and her child might nurse at her breast. And while her impatient child plucked her flowers to pick apart their colors, she waited for them to bloom into fruit and cooled the fruits under the kitchen tap and prepared them on the cutting board into slices for her husband to swallow into the apple of his throat, which she would kiss with her human lips.

At first, Yeou had supposed the trick behind her mother's transformation was love, so she rubbed her mother's petals on the dip between her brows and the point of her nose and the ridge between her lips and chin, and dipped her fingers in her mother's nectar and suckled on her fingertips, all in hopes of luring a butterfly to grant her their blessing. Yet in her attempt to recapture the curl of her tongue against another's, and so repeat her theft of the marble with her eyes firmly shut from the sight of both earth and heaven, Yeou found no respite beneath her mother's leaves, her mother's arms too thin to form a canopy, and found no comfort in her mother's embrace, her bark a poor substitute for warmth. Neither could her mother nurse an animal at her breast, nor feed it apples without cutting her fingers on its teeth, nor scratch behind its ears without tangling her roots in its fur and scraping away the flesh beneath.

Stars align, her mother had said, more often than lovers do, just as the lines that cross one's palms rarely intersect with each other, though her husband had always been able to trace a straight line across both his palms, which she'd taken as a premonition of his great fortune. For that reason, she'd followed him across the ocean, his line a compass needle pointing towards the vanishing point, his destination the endless elsewhere. He'd stolen her from her homeland like the seeds in the apple core stuck in his throat, and he had planted her in the garden of their new home, where she had taken root in the imperfect soil of his dream in an attempt to make it her own. Yet he had feet where she had roots, and he had wings where she had feet, and like the vanishing point, she could never reach him no matter how far she ventured herself. This, she told her child, was why he'd crossed over the ocean again in his quest to find a familiar face in his reflection in the water, which was only a trick of the sky. And as the birds flew out of the funeral hall, her mother told her that her greatest fear was of someday having to bury her child like she had buried her husband, and of fitting a fox in a casket meant for something taller or a human in a box too small for her shape, and so her greatest hope was to die before her child and be relieved of such fears forever.

In this way, the path of their hopes and their fears had always crossed over, but never intersected. This was the truth behind their change in shape: a human might become a fox or a tree, or a fish might become a bird, the way a clearing might be dug up to form a burial mound or a mountain might collapse into a crater, but when viewed from above and below, the fox marble was only a marble, and the sights inside were merely images captured in glass, illusions cast by the emptiness inside it, which was the hunger of the marble for a more perfect shape.

Yeou crawled in the direction of the unfurling world. She licked at the edge of her teeth and found them square. She imagined her mother must have always been a tree, just as Nabi must have always been a butterfly, just as her father must have always been dead or else waiting to die. She recalled Nabi's profile with her wings outstretched. She pictured the patterns of the wings themselves. Then the antennae she'd once felt curl to taste the hint of flowers from her forehead and her nose and slip between her lips. She shut her eyes and breathed new life into the memory. This was how Nabi had caught Yeou's mouth in her own. This was how Nabi had stolen the marble from under Yeou's tongue. This was how Nabi had licked up the nectar from her lips and pulled the marble from her mouth, which was an apple in Nabi's hand, which she'd fed to Yeou, and under the skin, the apple had tasted like meat or a promise from another world, which Yeou had returned to Nabi's mouth so they might sate their appetites together.

Bite by bite, the core of the apple had been exposed, and Yeou plucked the seeds from it and dug holes in the dirt with her sticky fingers to plant the seeds in fresh soil. This was how the tears that slipped from her eyes became rain, and the reflection of the rapture in her eyes became the boundary between this world and the promise of what lay beyond it, and the arch of her back became the curve of the horizon. And in her release, the heat caught in the crook of her fingers became the warmth of another dawn, and the soft hairs beneath her grip on the back of her neck became the texture of new grass, her pleasure a river, her teeth river stones, the curl of her toes the grip of roots in the soil, and the peak of her delight the crown of a tree, which quickened flowers into the fruit of this new knowledge: how a garden might emerge from the world into the world anew.

KYLE MARBUT

Four Poems from Black Swan Theory

The water I draw from the well may come up wine, but I still have to scrape my plates clean nightly like anyone else. Before every meal I swallow pictures of my mother at ever, at after, at rest. The hour, inconsistent. Caught dozing again in the light with a mouthful of what. Full sun fixed in nocturne, wreathed nightly in the galaxy arm. No moon. The only one I could tell is lost in the mirror. Her brow, my brow; my lid, her eye.

Sister, were we early. Sister, were we late. We lost every star to day, and another night is not promised. Once left, I spoke in our mother's voice just to hear it. With your eyes closed, you would mistake me for her or any other god. I swallowed that tongue, another draught, moonshine cut with winterberry. What I crave more than death, numb lightning, candlelight infinite in parallel windows. If this voice were really hers, I would wish for a second, truer sun.

I'm through with amazement! I don't mean to sound so sure, but the flowers are getting to me. One tree sheds its blossoms, another bursts open in its place. Long season of color so desperate for touch we don stripes and stroke from stamen to pistil. How to explain lack to such plenty. Mouthfuls of dead bees, sexless haze of slow ecodeath. Rabid hounds snap their jaws at low branches of dogwoods. Finches pluck weeping cherries bald en masse. Streets lined with Callery pears, fruitless and reeking of cum. The unbearable rain of petals. Close the blinds. A vision: petrified trunks shade a field aflame, smoke aglow in infinite sunset, lovers fossilized in ash. It's useless to behold endings as if they have already happened. Doom, too, is a hunger.

Dressed in just your blue jockstrap, you come to me whirling through the graveyard. Bearing honeycomb and black lace veils, foam at the mouth. Not the moonlight but what's beneath it makes the night real. If the moon is still there while I'm looking at you, I'll summer away the midnights you, drunk on cosmos, called my name wrong. Sight is only a measure of distance. Through every window I spy you heaving secrets behind the sunflowers. Darling, don't tell me you ate another star! You'll spoil your winter.

MIKE McCLELLAND

Is the Sky Falling or Are We Rising Towards the Lord?

The first church to ascend rose in rambling loops, slow but determined, a beanstalk growing towards the sun. Many followed, sometimes as many as forty or fifty churches in a day, though it appeared only one church per town made the cut. This seemed terribly unfair, particularly when Bezaleel, New Jersey's one rickety steeple took off on the same day as Manhattan's 23rd Street Synagogue.

News channel helicopters desperately chased the churches into the sky, but no one ever discovered where they went. Satellites didn't see them leave the Earth; no rubble was ever found. Rather than fade away, an ascending church simply became harder to detect.

Then it would be gone.

Church is the wrong word, really. Place of worship would be more accurate, perhaps. Churches, temples, synagogues, mosques, and cathedrals were taken. Some groups who will remain nameless (okay, it was the Baptists) were offended when the numbers were crunched and it was found that the distribution of religions among those chosen was very close to that of the general population. The numbers got a bit muddled when agnosticism was factored in, but the truth was there simply weren't many places agnostics gathered *as* agnostics.

After a week of ascensions, the consensus was that the most devout place of worship in any particular municipality was the one chosen to rise up. And even though this argument had plenty of evidence to back it, there was, of course, evidence to the contrary. Isn't there always? The methodology for measuring devotion varies greatly from person to person.

It all happened that autumn, which had a certain romance to it, but the Christians, particularly those whose churches hadn't ascended, feared that the coming Easter season would be anticlimactic. Jesus had ascended forty days after his death, which sent armchair theologists and historians into a frenzy of Internet sleuthing as they tried to figure out what had happened forty days before the first church rose out of Estcourt Station, Maine, but nothing they could find seemed to warrant such an astounding shift in the balance of what was known to be possible and not.

Can a phenomenon have anomalies? Isn't a phenomenon an anomaly itself? Can smaller wonders sprout from larger wonders like the eyes on a potato? Because there existed a few of both.

No churches rose from the village of Charlemont, Massachusetts. Instead, a mass of roots, soil, and rock erupted out of the nearby Mohawk Trail State Forest. Only a few grainy photos of this ascension exist, but witnesses claim to have seen a furry, oak-sized, hoofed leg kicking furiously out from within the ball of earth as it sped into the sky.

In Poughkeepsie, New York, the rising church was The Father's House, which sat in a strip mall between the Serenity Grace Beauty Parlor and a long-abandoned Radio Shack. It was the basement of The Father's House that rose first, breaking out through the parking lot, causing The Father's House to plunge backwards before it was dragged, upside down, into the heavens. The Father's House took the rest of the strip mall with it, twisting the ugly stretch of the shopping center like DNA. Horrified shoppers watched from the ground as the patrons of Serenity Grace—many of them mid-perm—clung to their styling chairs for dear life. The thing is, no one knew—or admitted to knowing—that The Father's House even *had* a basement.

On Newport, Rhode Island's Ascension Day, the members of the Newport Country Club sipped morning scotches and mimosas as they eagerly waited to see what kind of establishment would float away. A few people placed bets. It should have been a surprise, but it wasn't really—at least not to those watching from the Newport Country Club—when Newport's International Tennis Hall of Fame erupted into the sky, along with all twenty of its tennis courts.

Dear Parishioners,

It is my pleasure to inform you that, in light of recent events, the Pennsylvania Game Commission has approved our emergency request to lower the minimum age for junior hunting licenses from twelve to six and to move Pithole's hunting season up four full weeks. Furthermore, the Pithole Central School District has agreed to excuse all student hunters from school up through Ascension Day.

As such, we request that all persons in your household ages six and up immediately apply for a hunting license. The church has borrowed a few hundred rifles for the season, so please come down and sign one or more out at your earliest convenience. No ID required. We all know your blessed faces!

While we are happy to accept the fruits of your labors as gifts to the church, or to count them towards your tithes, we are also in the position to pay $100 per doe, $300 per female fawn, $500 per buck, and $1,000 per male fawn or yearling. It isn't our intent to make a political point about the value of one of the two genders, but we feel that God will find those sacrifices with the greatest breeding potential to be the most valued.

Bring your haul straight to the loading dock out back of the church, where volunteers will collect them and take them to the altar. Mary Lou will handle the financials.

Pithole is located in Wildlife Management Unit (WMU) 1A, which yields Pennsylvania's largest annual deer harvest. The Game Commission is anticipating a harvest of 30,000 this year and has granted us the generous cap of 5,000 deer for our sacrifice. We would like to meet that cap. So take your children, your wives, your mothers and fathers and cousins. Take the family dog. Get out there and let blood flow into God's fertile soil! Unleash the Calvary Cavalry! Surely, such a sacrifice will attract the Lord's benevolent grip.

On Eagle's Wings,
Big Jim
Calvary Baptist

The first hot pink line of sunlight slashed across the frosty, misty fields surrounding Pithole's Custaloga Forest, where dozens of children from ages six to sixteen carried loaded rifles. They were all after the same thing: a young buck. Only two male yearlings had been spotted the week they had to hunt for the Calvary Baptist sacrifices, and neither had been shot.

It was the day that would surely be Pithole's Ascension Day: November 1, the day after Halloween, and due to an unusually warm autumn, Pithole's trees still carried most of their leaves. A canopy of blazing orange, yellow, red, and purple soared above them and sent vivid confetti down into the fields as the children swung their guns back and forth in alarm.

Their mothers and fathers had mostly satisfied their bloodlust with does and girl-fawns and the occasional buck, but the children were in it to win. $1,000—or $2,000!—was an unfathomable amount of money to them and the thought of bringing the most valuable sacrifice into the church, where they would be adored and praised by their parents and Big Jim, was simply too tantalizing.

The children skittered unevenly towards the forest like a line of crabs at the crest of a wave-splashed dune. Frosted grass crunched under their feet, the shattering sound of it calling out in stark relief to the constant swishing of their orange Gore-Tex hunting gear.

Branches snapped underfoot as they entered Custaloga Forest, where every shaking branch and fallen trunk looked like a proud young buck. Someone screamed, "There they are!" Everyone assumed *they* were the two yearlings. Shots rang out. It was impossible for any hunter to know if the bullets were coming from in front of them or behind, from their left or their right.

Bullets beget bullets, and the shots erupted with increasing frequency. Branches exploded, birds shrieked, squirrels fled. The smartest of the little humans ducked for cover.

To an outsider, anyone unfamiliar with hunting season in Pithole, this scene might have seemed as extraordinary as an ascending church. Certainly as terrifying. But the truth of the matter was that this was simply another hunting day in Pithole. The hunters were younger perhaps, and the stakes higher, but the rain of bullets, the sense of camaraderie and competition and bloodlust, the mystery of the cold woods in the early morning were constants. That was just Pithole.

On the day that would surely be Pithole's Ascension Day, two boys met at Shady Shade Skate Park. Both had wet hair. Ben had come straight from football practice, and Zip had showered five times in preparation for meeting Ben.

"Hi," Zip said, trying to smile in a way that was attractive and confident and friendly, but also a little cool and distant because he didn't want to look like he cared too much, even though he cared more about this than he'd ever cared about anything else.

"Hi," Ben said, noting how beautiful Zip looked with the vivid leaves falling down around him. Beautiful despite his terrified expression, which was filled with a kind of anxiety that was very familiar to Ben at that moment.

Before this, the two boys had never spoken a single word to each other. They'd made full eye contact on three occasions: on the hellish first day of ninth grade; then again on the night when Ben scored a touchdown at homecoming their junior year and—helmet tossed, smile huge—looked over to the marching band where Zip was staccato-ing G major chords on his keyboard in applause; and finally in study hall on the Tuesday before Ascension Day, when Zip pressed the blue Post-it that read "Skate Park 8:30 AM Friday?" into Ben's hand with shaking fingers.

Pithole wasn't the kind of place where one came out of the closet. Zip thought of himself as openly gay in the sense that he assumed his parents and his sister Kaya and his best friends already knew, but it wasn't something they talked about. Ben, on the other hand, had seen the toxic combination of judgment, pity, and curiosity his Uncle Ned had suffered as an openly gay man in their family and in Pithole at large and had no interest in following in his footsteps. The only gay people Ben had ever met were Uncle Ned, Ned's ex-boyfriend Ismail, Sergeant Murphy, and the lesbians who owned the used bookstore.

Both boys had friends waiting in churches all over town. Friends who had chosen to go, friends who had been dragged by their parents, friends who simply wanted to see the miracle up close. Ben's mother had tried to shove him into her Ford Expedition, which had his father, grandparents, and three siblings packed inside it, ready to head to First

Christian for a prayer-a-thon and bake sale they hoped would attract the Lord's lifting hand. Zip's mother, his aunts, his uncles, and twenty-three of his first cousins had all been at Pithole Korean Presbyterian's pop-up soup kitchen since 5 AM and had cumulatively sent him 237 texts asking him where he was. His father had tried to bribe him into going to Bethel AME that morning.

In the weeks since the first ascension had taken all four residents of Estcourt Station skyward, friends and family had begged both boys to go to church on Ascension Day. To save their souls, to live forever, to wash their sins away, to greet a new dawn, they said.

Ben had been silent, and Zip had refused. Neither had rebelled out of any particular protest against religion, or even the skepticism they usually felt for the faithful.

No, both boys stayed away from church because both realized they had been waiting. And what was the point of waiting when you could be plucked up into the beyond at any second? Zip realized that if he disappeared before he ever allowed himself to be himself, then his self would never have existed. Ben wondered what the point of being forgiven was if he had never even sinned.

Pithole, Pennsylvania, had nineteen official places of worship. Twenty, if you counted Lady Dierdre's Emporium of Esoterica. Seventeen of the churches were Christian, including six Catholic, three nondenominational Restorationist, and two Presbyterian churches. Those denominations with only one establishment were the Unitarians, Methodists, Mennonites, Episcopalians, African Methodist Episcopalians, and Baptists. Then there was the Pithole Jewish Community Center up by the college and the Islamic Society of Northwestern Pennsylvania to the southeast, just within the city's limits.

There were old grudges and conflicts between certain churches, but nothing severe. There was a long-running rivalry between the Catholics, particularly between St. Hippolyte's folksy country congregation and St. Agnieszka's wealthier, town-dwelling parishioners. There was also an odd tension between Wesley Way Methodist and First

Presbyterian, whose active youth groups seemed to recruit from the same pool of young Pitholians.

When news of the ascensions hit, Pithole's churches launched into a festival of giving, helping, praying, and service. Homeless people were swept off the streets and into spare bedrooms and repurposed broom closets. Park benches were mended and lacquered; graffiti was painted over. The hungry suddenly found their refrigerators overflowing with the best the Walmart Superstore had to offer. The Unitarians had taken to fasting, while St. Bonita's hosted a massive Last Supper. Both had competitors who mimicked and tried to outdo them, because it wasn't enough to do *as well* as one's holy neighbor. Only one church would rise!

All of Pithole's churches became 24-hour centers of activity.

Well, all except one.

Tia Dixon had been the pastor at Pithole's Bethel AME Church for over a decade. As the only church in town with a Black majority among its congregation, Tia felt a particular responsibility to make Bethel AME a true sanctuary. A place of peace and rest during a time when there was little of either for Black people, particularly in a place like Pithole, where ninety percent of the population was whiter than bone.

She'd been preaching the same message from the day the first church had ascended, but she threw everything she had into it the morning of Pithole's Ascension Day. She wound her braids heavenward in her signature beehive, put on her favorite white robe, and despite the season, donned her Lenten purple stole. She marched right up to the pulpit. There would be no music today. There would be no refreshments. After the service, the doors would be locked.

"My friends, my family, my sisters and brothers, I'm going to make this short and fast," she said, her voice commanding attention. "Get the hell out of here."

The congregation—most of whom were lapsed members who had returned to Bethel as if Ascension Day were Christmas or Easter—gaped at her.

"Go!" she said. "You don't need to listen to the whole sermon. I'll email it to you."

A few people stood and walked out, but not enough.

Tia pulled all the air she could into her lungs. She channeled all of her power into her voice. She opened her mind for prayer and hoped she would be a conduit for the True Word.

"I understand why the rest of you are waiting. You are waiting to see if this is a test. This whole event has warped you into thinking there is some exclusivity to God's love. That God only wants a small portion of us. But you are underestimating God. God is bigger than you can imagine. God has room for everyone. God doesn't have a favored one percent." Tia reached into herself. "There is no mystery to God's love, my friends. There is no test to pass. You just have it. So when I tell you to run, please run. If this building gets plucked up from the Earth, I don't want a single one of you inside it when it does. Our church is not a building. It's every one of you. Take our church and go bask in the immensity of God's love. Now, please. Run."

They were on each other in seconds. Neither boy had any real experience. Zip had never kissed anyone, and Ben's romantic interactions had been limited to chaste pecks from his long-suffering girlfriend, Lauryn. But now they were fueled by apocalyptic urgency and years of percolating attraction. They smashed their lips together. Zip was taller, and he awkwardly put his hands on Ben's shoulders, then his cheeks, before wrapping them around the center of Ben's back, which made him feel like he was carrying a large box somewhere. Ben, his aim truer, put his hands on Zip's ass.

They both recognized they were kissing too hard, a combination of tongue torque and tooth, which necessitated a break after only a minute or so.

"Your eyes are pretty up close," Ben said, kicking himself for saying *pretty*. "Handsome," he corrected. "Impressive. Striking. Hot?"

"Why are white people obsessed with eye color?" Zip said, but then he gave Ben a reassuring peck. "You're so strong," he said, rubbing his hands up and down Ben's arms. Ben wasn't *that* strong, but Zip figured a football player would want to hear how nice his muscles were.

Despite the profound awkwardness they both felt, there was no question that this was what they had been waiting for.

"I've always liked you," Zip said.

Ben squeezed Zip's ass.

"Why haven't we been doing this for years?" he asked.

Ben reluctantly let go and grabbed Zip's hand, a move that felt weirdly intimate. He pulled Zip up to the deck of the skate park's half-pipe, where they could see the roofs of the municipal buildings and the spires of the churches that surrounded Park Square. He sat on the edge and let his feet dangle and patted the space next to him.

Zip sat and smiled when he saw that he and Ben were the same height sitting down. It was easier to kiss now. He let his long pianist fingers dance up Ben's sides and over his shoulders and into the shorter boy's sandy hair. Despite the fact that they were sitting down, Ben's hand found Zip's ass again.

The rumble could be felt for miles and miles, well beyond Pithole's city limits. Oil—thought to have been tapped out in the region years ago—burst from beneath the solemn statue in the center of Park Square. The statue was of two sleeping grouses with their heads at rest upon each other's necks, which created a feathered infinity loop connecting the birds' squat bodies. The statue fell to the side as the oil shot upward, creating a vertical black river at the heart of Pithole.

Later, witnesses would claim to have seen any number of things emerge from the pillar of oil. The most widely spotted oddity—and as such, maybe the most believable—was the immaculately preserved bodies of two long-dead men embracing each other in the same fashion as the statue's grouses.

But the oil and the bodies were not the only things that rose. A tuba—more discerning eyes would have correctly identified it as a euphonium—erupted from out of the back window of Custaloga College's conservatory's storeroom. The dusty silver horn sounded a plaintive note as the instrument rocketed towards the heavens. Many would report that seven trumpets played that day, but it was really just the one euphonium.

Edwina Bueno claimed that the electric blue gown she'd been trying on at Buttons & Bows Secondhand Coature had been ripped from her body just as she'd begun to pull up its zipper. The dress, she said, fled of its own accord (or, she later corrected, the Lord's) and burst out the front door of Buttons & Bows and took to the sky. Her story was corroborated by several other shoppers as well as the shopkeeper, Jolene Killmyers.

Survivors would mention other ascending oddities. Two lean bucks, young but majestic, leaped out of Custaloga Forest and never returned to the ground, their noble horns catching the sun as they zoomed heavenward. A tarpaulin with the words "Art Tent" spray-painted on its side floated up out of Camp Woodcock. A dozen Little League trophies shot through the wall of UStorageA. A wide silver bowl broke through the window of a house in The Bluffs and made it a few hundred feet in the air before whatever force was behind its ascension decided that it didn't really want the bowl after all. It fell back to Earth, leaving a small crater in the middle of Washington Avenue. A huge pumpkin lifted off the porch of an eerily empty Victorian home just off of Custaloga College's campus and rolled into the sky, seemingly growing and glowing like Cinderella's carriage. At one point it was as if a second sun were blinking in and out of sight.

All of it—the mummified men, the horn, the dress, the bucks, the tarp, the trophies, the pumpkin-carriage—became impossible to discern. The river of oil spilling out of Pithole thinned and thinned until it was merely a black mist. Then, with one last belch, the last of the oil shot out of the ground, punctuating the screams of Pithole's residents.

Ben climbed on top of Zip, straddling him on the hard, smooth wood of the halfpipe's deck. Zip forgot everything: his name, his sore back, the fact that today would surely be Pithole's Ascension Day. All he knew was that he would sooner allow his jaw to fall off than stop kissing Ben. How did anyone ever do anything other than kiss? Once you'd done it, how did you stop? Once you felt the way Zip was feeling now, why would you want to feel anything else? Ben felt it, too—behind his nose. It took him a minute to realize he was about to cry.

Neither boy was surprised when the skate park began to rise.

Pithole fell away beneath them.

Lady Dierdre D'Avalon (born Denise Butters) had not been looking forward to Ascension Day. Not one bit. Business had gone up 500% since places of worship had started to ascend. Everyone was buying incense, sage, candles, and crystals. So many goddamn crystals.

It wasn't just the money, though that surely helped. It was the acceptance. One day Dierdre had been the local crackpot, catering mostly to rebelling teenagers and housewives in the middle of lowkey life crises, and now her shop was a legitimate hub of community activity.

She had just finished braiding a little girl's hair into a protective, eight-braided plait when she heard the screams. She picked up her velveteen skirts and tromped out into the shop's small parking lot, where the girl's mother and brother were pointing at a black river in the sky. Dierdre ran back into the shop, pulled out her can of Morton's, and poured a circle of salt around her feet. She stood there, frozen, as all of the candles in her shop lit of their own accord.

An antique iron fox mask Dierdre had purchased at a local estate sale began to shake in the display case beneath the counter. She watched in horror as it lifted off its cushion. She reached into the case and snatched the mask, pulling it into her salt circle.

"Absolutely not!" she yelled at the ceiling.

Her tarot deck, still on the counter from an earlier reading, began to vibrate. A card shot from the deck and slapped itself down onto the counter. It was The Magician, her wand pointed skyward. The card signified that Earth was a reflection of Heaven. *As above, so below.*

"No shit," Dierdre said and pinched the bridge of her nose.

Another card flew from her deck.

The Wheel of Fortune. Greater forces at work.

"I get the picture," said Dierdre.

A third card. This one: The Tower.

Destruction. The consequence of unchecked human ambition.

The hairs on the back of Dierdre's neck stood up.

"Oh fuck," she said.

It was a three-card reading: past, present, future. The Magician, The Wheel of Fortune, The Tower. Its meaning shot into Dierdre's head like cold lightning.

What goes up must come down.

News channel helicopters raced up from Pittsburgh, down from Buffalo, and over from Cleveland to record the aftermath of what had occurred at Pithole. It was an anomaly within a phenomenon. What had once been Pithole, Pennsylvania, was now just a pit. Or a hole.

Some would speculate that the loss of oil reserves underneath Pithole had destabilized the town and caused it to fall. But the majority surmised that Pithole's descent revealed an opposing force to whatever was plucking places of worship into the sky. Was it the Devil? Was it the Earth herself?

There were survivors, of course. Some people found themselves impossibly transported outside city limits. They blinked and were suddenly far away at a much later time. The Islamic Society was entirely spared, though it now perched on the edge of a cliff rather than the edge of the town. Several preschools were found two counties over in the pastures of Maple Row Dairy. Lady Dierdre and several members of the Jewish Community Center and the Mennonite Church wound up in the public house of a Renaissance faire forty-five miles down Interstate 79.

But many more were lost.

And then there were the two boys.

All that was left of Pithole proper was Shady Shade Skate Park, which sat on a lone spire of rock, Pithole having fallen around it. The two boys were marooned there until they were rescued by Pittsburgh's Channel 4 Newscopter.

The ground was still giving way around the edges of what had been

Pithole, so the helicopter landed on a flat-topped hill a few miles north of town. The day was clear enough that Ben and Zip could see the pulsing, crumbling canyon in the distance and Shady Shade Skate Park poking out of it like a nose hair. As they stood there and stared, a Channel 4 anchor attempted to interview the boys.

When the anchor asked what it all meant, why they had been spared when so much of Pithole had fallen, the boys shared a long look.

"What does it mean?" the anchor repeated, holding out his microphone.

Ben didn't know if he was supposed to look at the anchor or the camera or the microphone. He thought about making a hole joke, but it didn't seem like the time, all things considered, so he just shook his head.

The anchor huffed and flapped his hands at the camerawoman, then turned back to the boys.

"But what does it *mean*?" he asked again.

Ben looked at Zip, and Zip shrugged.

CHRISTOPHER NELSON

Theology

said the blade to the lamb we're in this together said the garden to the god when do we have a say said the lamb in return yes but only one of us is an exit said the poet to the moon none or few but you & you O you said the god to the garden I give you locusts and you give me your yearning said the moon in reply why said the sayer to the said we bled with a pity unique to men said the men in chorus know you not the principle of the knot the one that binds & the one that gives said the garden to the man without me you're just another animal said the animal to the god we know you like the smell of water said the water the only word, house & seed of all others, the unspliced root the mother even of god who set down the gavel & astrolabe to try her hand at gardening to be green again after so much silence so much noise in the code

REUBEN GELLEY NEWMAN

Dear Dear

1.

The dog-eared copy of *Autobiography of Red*
seemed like something archival to him,
smudged with the fingerprints of who knows how many boys
and perhaps some charcoal and semen,
so of course he lingered in the library with the Hershey's Kisses
left over from Valentine's Day and the vague reminisces
of the potatoes he parboiled and roasted for dinner
with a smattering of cumin and paprika,
all doused in maple syrup and some mundane
brand of Argentinian olive oil,
a few carrots thrown in for luck, roasted to the point of burning,
because burning is what every boy wants,
especially when they are alone
and it is winter.

2.

He is cooking meat
for the first time. Initially
there is nothing much to it:
tossing the boneless thighs
into the pot to braise,
then waiting until the flesh
absorbs the memories
of kale striving in some
industrial farm under
acres of mechanized sunlight.
Next time he will dig his hands

into the chicken, marinate it
in lemon juice and olive oil
with spices, or lay wings to crackle
on a sheet pan. He was never
a vegetarian but now
he eats meat like a man.
After all, he has grown.
He has grown up.

3.

His brain marinates marvelously
in the winter air, as if there is
a bubble of thought brimming with glimmers
of ice haloing him.
He decides to live against desire.
He decides to make a snow angel
and freeze for hours in the absence
of desire. Then he goes to his job at the library where he retrieves
book after book from the stacks
with dry titles he can't remember. Except
somebody asks for *Coraline*.

4.

Living against desire is a joke.
Or so he thinks, one afternoon,
when deer prints garnish
the fresh snow as he goes out
to do the laundry. Having
masturbated. Having showered.
Having not done the laundry
for two weeks. He still thinks of himself
as a boy even though by all rights and purposes
he is a man. If the poem is a diary,
he is a princess. If the poem

is an elegy, he is a monk. If the poem is a mask,
he is a goddamn faggot and he does his nails
in brilliant purple before plucking a pen
from perfectly coiffed hair.

5.

As a kid he dressed up. Or played dress-up.
Played at being that princess. Cinderella was his favorite.
The purple silk skirt, tattered hem, his grandmother made him.
Fucking nostalgia. The prerogative of queers.
The past is mythic. You're on the yellow brick road,
following breadcrumbs to Troy.

6.

He is alone. It is winter. He walks through the forest
in old sneakers after the thaw, having failed
to realize the slush is still married to the ground.
His shoes get soaked, drunk on the early
arrival of spring. False, assuredly.
Yet fifty-degree weather does a happy fairy make.
The yellow birches continue peeling poems
comprised of their skin. The beech woods loiter,
bemused in youthful arrogance. A reticent
volcano lurks beyond the next hilltop.
A dragon lives inside it. A deer flashes
through the maples and the fairy burns
with desire. He can't wait for roast venison
at the dragon's Sunday brunch.
He supposes he has a crush.
Will the dragon eat him for breakfast?
Will the dragon make love to him at night?
So many exciting possibilities!

7.

He climbs to the top of Vesuvius, sifts through pumice stone.
He is with his Latin class. It is his junior year of high school.
Spring. He has so much left to learn about love.

8.

The chicken stew grows bones.
A ghost chicken rises from burnt
splatters between the stovetop spirals.
When he cuts off its head, it goes running
amok in the griddle garden. Invisible blood.
Two heads grow back. He takes the chicken as
a present to the dragon. Here, he says, a two-headed
ghost chicken. Isn't that exciting? (More exciting than
roast venison!) Cluck, cluck, goes the chicken. Meh,
I've seen better, goes the dragon. Alrighty,
goes the boy. Suddenly he feels very cold. Invisible boys get
invisibly disappointed. Turns out a chicken isn't a great present.
The dragon would have preferred gold.

9.

Isn't it a fairy tale: he walks home and suddenly it's snowing.
How it drapes the trees. How pretty he is. The beard
that drapes his face. How learned and literary. If
the poem is ironic, it's also terribly earnest. If
it's an exercise in fancy, it's also a play
with mundanity. Dear boy, my darling.
Dear boy—oh dear.
Dear, dear, dear, dear.

CAROLYN OLIVER

From Her Tulip Bower Tommelise Writes the Swallow

Dear Swallow, how is a hollow mended?
The gilded wings he pledged were barely floss
enough to lift a raindrop's song. He fed me wind
and bone. Starved, I learned to swim.

Dear Swallow, seems every sailor I met carried
your shadow on his skin. For my daily bread
I mapped your curves, my thighs corbiculae
a-rasp with pollen. Honey I couldn't send.

Dear Swallow, the moth tendered me a morsel,
her only night. Ravenous, I dreamt your claws
gone manacle. At dawn, soft scales painted
my bare wrists. No key in any of her eyes.

Dear Swallow, in my roofless room I lie
restless, fastened to rumor. How swift you've
become, tearing through the small hours.
How immaculate your feasts.
How your silence

swallows me.

—I believed your elegance a net.
I believed you wanted eggs red as meat
or blue as sleep. I believed I knew
what leaving meant.

Swallow.

Dear glutton. Dear banquet. Dear grace.
This bower's for breaking.
Your hunger waits.

CAT POWELL

What's He Building in There

After Tom Waits

Your father has been spending a lot of time in the basement recently, and I'm hoping you will speak with him about this. I know you keep saying you won't get involved in things between us anymore, but he is your father and I am concerned. On the one hand, at least he's not following me around the house watching me do chores like he did in the early months of his retirement. On the other hand, it is concerning. When I say a lot of time, I mean *a lot* of time. Please call or email him. I think he is lonely and possibly depressed.

I saw the photos you posted on the Facebook. I'm glad that you are having fun, but I feel like if you have time to post those photos, you have time to at least email your father.

You are right. That email was passive aggressive. See? I can "evolve," too. Unlike your father. The other day I had to explain to him what passive aggressive meant, and then when we were in line at the supermarket he turned to the perfect stranger behind us and said, "I'm passive aggressive. Do you know what that means?" I wanted to crawl under the candy rack.

I think you have a point about social isolation not doing him any favors. He does sometimes go to watch the game and have a pitcher with Ted, but that relationship isn't very deep. I don't think he's had any close friends since his brother died.

I'm glad to hear that work is going well, but don't forget that your career is only one part of your life. And not the part that's going to give me grandkids! Just kidding. (Haha, not really.) The decorations for Sherri's baby shower arrived yesterday. I think they're going to look really nice. I'll send you pictures once I get them up.

Don't be silly! You can't throw your own daughter's baby shower! That's why I did Sherri's for Margene. (It went well, by the way. Pictures attached.) Honestly, if the topic upsets you that much, maybe it's time to revisit the idea of freezing your eggs. You're clearly not taking dating seriously, and I told you we could use some of the money we set aside for your wedding. Maybe one of your gay friends could be a sperm donor.

Honestly, that is probably a much better idea than trying to raise a child with a straight man. It's not all it's cracked up to be. Your father, for example, is still obsessed with his mystery project in the basement. He never came to bed Saturday night, and when I woke up, the truck was gone. Then an hour later he was back with a truck bed full of sheet-rock panels. I told him he was going to destroy his back carrying them by himself, but he said he'd be fine, he was wearing a belt. You know how he is about hiring help for anything. Remember the fuse box?

He did manage to get the panels down, though—with a lot of bumping and cursing. Then he stayed down in the basement all day. When I called him for dinner, he didn't answer. So I finally went down there and found him lying flat on his back on the floor in literal agony. He said he was just resting, but when he tried to get up, he couldn't. He wouldn't let me call an ambulance or even a neighbor, so I brought him some ice packs and Advil and tried to make him comfortable. I couldn't help pointing out that none of this would have happened if he'd hired the neighbor kid, and he said that kids these days don't know how to do a job properly and it would have been like lighting money on fire. I was tempted to tell him that a broken back is a lot more expensive than an hour of a teenager's time, but I thought about what you said about boundaries and bit my tongue.

Aren't you proud of me?

Tonya stopped by yesterday. Lisa is in New York now, too! She's doing her surgical residency at Mt. Sinai, and Tonya went down for her engagement party last weekend. You should look her up on the Facebook. Also, Mary-Louise's daughter Bertha—remember her? You met her at the MacCrae's barbecue two summers ago—is pregnant. Don't tell anyone because she's still in her first trimester, but Mary-Louise was too excited to keep it in.

I'm having Mitch and Cindy over for dinner on Friday. I was thinking I'd see if Shelby's had any good fish, but it can be tricky cooking fish for company, so maybe I'll do a roast instead. I'll have to see what we have in the deep freeze. If your father ever lets me back in the basement. He's become very territorial about it.

I think that is a really rude thing to say about Lisa! I'm sure she's grown up a lot since you knew her. I mean, my God, remember the bangs you had back then, before you grew into your forehead?

Yes, your father is still spending most of his time in the basement, and honestly that may be for the best. When he does come upstairs, he's very cranky, and he snapped at me this morning because there wasn't any jerky in the pantry, when he knows it's Monday and I do the shopping on Tuesdays. I told him he's been eating too much of it anyway. All that salt cannot be good for his heart.

I am sorry you feel I've been overly critical of your appearance. It was just clear to me early on that you were going to be very pretty and I didn't want you to get a big head about it. And yes, you are correct that your father is a grown man and can buy his own jerky, though he seems increasingly reluctant to go anywhere that isn't the basement. On that note, it's November 1, which means we need to discuss Thanksgiving. Maybe you'd like to bring a guest?

I am now officially banned from the basement. I tried to go down yesterday to get the roast out of the deep freeze. No sooner had I opened the door than I was hit with an overpowering wave of paint fumes. I steeled myself and had gotten as far as the first landing when your father—who otherwise has been rather lethargic recently—came barreling up the stairs, practically lifting me right back out the door and into the front hall. He told me that it was still "in progress" and "not ready."

What is *it*, you may ask? Still no clue.

I told him I just wanted to see what meats were in the deep freeze. He came back a few seconds later with a pork loin and said that was all that was left, but I KNOW that freezer was FULL only a month ago. I think maybe he broke the freezer and is afraid to own up to it. Before the paint fumes, I'd been noticing an odd smell. Something musky. I'm hoping when you come home for Thanksgiving you will talk with him. Maybe you can get down there and investigate the source of the odor.

Maybe things were a little weird at Thanksgiving, yes. I will try to talk to your father about it sometime this week. Marriages aren't easy, you know. And this transition to retirement has been hard for him. The men of our generation don't seem to be thriving in this life stage. Lonnie's husband was so depressed after he retired that she almost had him committed. Then he got into macrame and started an Etsy shop, and now it looks like 1972 exploded in the middle of their living room. But at least he's not depressed anymore.

I am not being "avoidant." I just want to give your father some space to figure things out for himself. We've been together a long time. I'm sure we can get through this.

I thought more about what you said, and I decided to try to talk to your father. It did not go well. He kept yawning! I started to get really angry, so I got up to get some water and calm down, and when I got back, he was fast asleep on the living room couch. I shook him awake, but then he was too groggy to converse properly. I did, however, sneak down to the basement while he was asleep. He has somehow—God knows when—managed to clear out almost everything down there. He must be taking stuff to the dump while I'm asleep. I suppose it's an improvement from his hoarding days, though I don't understand why he's been so secretive when I have literally been begging him to do this for years. Anyway, the only pieces of furniture left are the deep freeze, empty and unplugged, and that old futon of yours from college I have repeatedly asked you to do something about. The futon is now in the center of the room, unfolded and covered with a heap of pillows and blankets. It looks like a nest. As for the contents of the deep freeze, who knows.

Aside from the nest, the rest of the basement is immaculate. He redid all the walls very nicely. He stenciled and spray-painted everything with these beautiful patterns. It looks like a forest scene, only a bit abstract. I don't quite know how to describe it, but it's lovely. Your father used to be a very artistic person.

I was careful not to disturb anything, but somehow he knew. As soon as he woke up, he went down there and then immediately came roaring back up to accuse me of meddling with his things. What things? There's practically nothing left! I denied it, but he said he could *smell* me down there. Clearly he's nuts. At least an hour had elapsed, and as you know, I am not a heavily scented person.

Maybe you can try to talk to him again at Christmas.

What do you mean you aren't coming home for Christmas? You're going to Patagonia? By yourself? This seems dangerous and ill-advised, but it's your life, I guess. All I did was birth, house, raise, and feed you, but by all means, don't feel like you owe me a Christmas visit.

Maybe your father does need therapy, but do you honestly think he will ever do that? In the meantime, I don't feel unsafe. I just do my best to keep out of his way, which is easy given that he stays in the basement ninety percent of the time. I wonder what he's up to now that the construction is finished. He's been sleeping down there, too. I'm guessing in that absurd futon nest, which I told him will only wreak further havoc on his back.

Lou Ellen was supposed to host a holiday-themed girls' night on Thursday, but a pipe burst and flooded her basement, so I volunteered. I haven't told your father yet. He's never really liked that crew. I'm hoping he'll just stay in the basement. Anyway, I should go because I have an absurd amount of baking to do before the party.

Well, your father did NOT stay in the basement, and now things have come to a head.

The party was going smoothly at the start. Lou Ellen came around six to help me set up, and we had a good chat about George. He still hasn't finished his dissertation. Maybe you could talk to him since you've been in and out of grad school so many times yourself.

The rest of the ladies arrived at seven. We had a lovely time for the first hour. Everyone had drinks and the mood was lively. Then I heard an ominous thumping coming from the basement stairs. "That must be Rick," I said. "He's been doing some home improvements in the basement." No sooner had I said it than your father bursts into the living room looking like a wild man, his hair disheveled, his face unshaven, his eyes bloodshot. He didn't even say hello! He just lumbered over to the food, grabbed a fistful of snack mix, and crammed it into his mouth. Then he snatched up the entire bowl and trundled back to the basement. Not a word the entire time. The ladies were speechless. I tried to laugh it off, but the mood never recovered and everyone left early, even Lou Ellen.

As I was washing the dishes, I started to get so angry. I mean, I have been very patient with this man's behavior. I don't think he's spoken more than three words to me in weeks. And now this crap, pardon my language. Spoiling my party with his rudeness! Do you think he might be doing drugs?

Anyway, I prepared myself to have it out with him and marched down to the basement, only to find him asleep again. I wasn't going to be evaded so easily, though. I shook him as hard as I could. He lolled onto his back and started to snore. I shouted right in his face, but that didn't wake him either. Then something in me snapped. I'd come down there to have it out with him, and I was going to have it out. He wasn't going to avoid me just by losing consciousness, that's for sure! I started in about how rude he'd been during the party. And in the weeks before that! And in the years before that! Once I started, I couldn't stop!

Maybe you had a point when you said I have a lot of pent-up rage I need to deal with.

I do love your father. He is a good man. And I respect that retirement is a hard transition. I appreciate all that he's done to take care of us over the years, and I know the physical decline is difficult. I think it generally hits men harder, and your father has always been proud of his physical strength. But at the same time, it's been almost a year now and he's acting like he's the only person who's ever had to reinvent himself. I went through it when I had you. And again when you left home. And again during menopause. Come to think of it, women are pretty much masters of reinvention. But these men! Imagine, sleeping in a futon nest!

There has been no further fallout because your father is still asleep. It's been several days now. Maybe he's waking up late at night while I'm in bed? If so, he's very good at covering his tracks. The jerky supply remains stable. His heartbeat is slow and steady, and he's breathing, but I cannot wake him no matter what I try. He seemed a little cool to the touch, so I took his temperature. Ninety degrees! I don't know what to make of that. I've been checking on him a couple of times a day and so far I haven't detected any other changes. Except for his beard, which continues to grow.

I know I should call a doctor. Do you think I'm a total idiot? But also, do you know how expensive ambulances are? I've been googling and there are some fascinating sleep disorders. I think your father might have Kleine-Levin syndrome. Although a common symptom is hypersexuality, and let me tell you, *that* certainly has not been your father's affliction these last few years! Aside from the sleeping and the low temperature, he honestly seems fine. Maybe he just needs a rest and reset or something.

He must be okay on some level because his hair is continuing to grow at an alarming rate. And not just on his head and face, but on his arms and hands too. Also, he seems to be getting fatter, which makes me think he must be sneaking upstairs when I'm not around. Maybe he's faking this whole thing, some kind of cry for help. I'm going to tell him that if he doesn't get up in the next forty-eight hours I'm calling an ambulance. That should scare him awake.

Thank you for sending the security camera, though it would have been better if you'd just come yourself. It took me the better part of the day to install it, and when I look at it on my phone now, nine times out of ten, it is pointing at the ground, so I have not been able to detect any signs of your father rousing himself. Vitals remain stable.

Susie G.—you know, who lives at the end of the cul-de-sac? You're always saying you don't know who anyone is, but I'm certain you know Susie—her son Bobby is a primary care doctor, and she told me yesterday that he'll be visiting this weekend. I'm thinking I'll see if he could pop over and have a look at your father. For all her faults, Susie G. is not a gossip, though she'll probably love having a secret to lord over me. Oh well. It would be nice if you would come, too. I'm pretty sure Bobby is still single.

You have a job interview in Los Angeles? My goodness. Well, I'm sure they have single doctors in California, too. Anyway, Susie G. assured me that Bobby would be happy to do a consult, and of course her lips are sealed.

I've been having a hard time controlling my irritation lately and have been keeping more to myself as a result. I feel calmest when I'm down in the basement with your father, weirdly. He's very pleasant company when he's unconscious. (I know you will laugh at this, but it's true!) I've been going to sit with him most afternoons.

Yesterday, in advance of Bobby's visit, I tried to groom your father a bit. I trimmed his beard and hair as best I could. Then I tried tackling his nails, which are now practically claws. This is going to sound odd, but I swear his hands have gotten bigger. Your father has always had large hands. Actually, that was one of the first things I was attracted to when we met. You'd think I'd know his hands pretty well after all these years, but holding them the weight felt different. Unfamiliar. Maybe it's just been a long time since we touched each other.

I had that thought while I was sitting there holding his hand, trying to cut through those ghastly nails. I thought, "It's been a long time since we touched each other," and then I started to cry. I can remember a day when your father's body was as familiar to me as my own. I guess that was a long time ago, but it doesn't feel that way. It feels like it only just happened. And that makes the strangeness of his hands now all the more shocking, in the same way that my face in the mirror is shocking, because wasn't I just twenty-three and in love and thinking the whole world would unfurl in front of me in endlessly beautiful and wonderful ways?

I will confess I felt a bit embarrassed after I sent that last email. You are so nice to say you appreciated it. I hope that's true.

In spite of my best attempts to groom your father, when I went down yesterday morning, his hair and nails had completely grown back. I didn't have time to do anything about it because Bobby was ringing the bell. Fifteen minutes early! He was wearing a Brooks Brothers button-down even though it was Saturday morning, and he had a stethoscope around his neck under his scarf. You did not miss anything on that front.

He did examine your father, though, and pronounced his symptoms to be concurrent with hibernation. Hibernation! "But humans don't hibernate," I told him. Bobby gave a little shrug, obviously trying to look confident while clearly out of his depth. I cannot stand people who won't admit when they don't know something. Bobby suggested I have your father taken to a hospital for more tests. That sounded expensive. I asked him if he thought your father was in immediate danger and he hemmed and hawed and gave a lot of disclaimers, but eventually he admitted he couldn't really see anything wrong, aside from the whole hibernating thing. Maybe we wait until Spring? I asked Bobby if he wanted coffee and immediately regretted the offer, but mercifully, he declined.

How did the interview go? Do you think you might take the job? Maybe Los Angeles would be a nice change of pace for you. This winter has been so miserable. We've had three straight days of sleet. Your father might be onto something with this whole hibernation thing.

Your father is noticeably larger. Not fatter—if anything, he seems to have burned off some of the pudge—but *larger*. His hands, his feet, even his head. It's so noticeable that I got my measuring tape from the sewing kit to confirm it. I'm tracking his measurements and will let you know. He's also covered in hair. You know your father has always had that very fine, northern European kind of hair, but this new hair is much coarser. Same color, that mousy brown with hardly any gray. Not like me. I went gray at forty. Cross your fingers that you inherited your father's hair, just like you inherited his straight teeth. Speaking of, his teeth seem larger, too.

I'm glad to hear the interview went well. Maybe I'll come spend the winters out in California if you move, especially if your father intends to continue with this hibernating business. If he doesn't wake up by April, I'll call an ambulance.

I'm sorry it's taken me a little while to get back to you. Your father's cleaning out of the basement inspired me to clear out the rest of the house. And with your father asleep, this is my big chance to redecorate *properly*. If I stick to my goals and get the upstairs done by the end of January, I'm going to hire painters. I think I deserve a treat.

I've been waking up around sunrise and cleaning until midday. Then I go down to sit with your father. The basement is cool and dry but not cold, and your father's presence is calming. Maybe because his breathing is so slow and steady. I brought one of the dining-room chairs down, and sometimes I knit, but mostly I just sit there. At first, I sat in silence, but then I tried speaking my thoughts aloud and found it was much nicer. Maybe part of your father's brain can still hear me. I wonder if he's dreaming. I googled "do animals dream when they hibernate" and found out that bears, for example, show very little brain activity at all when hibernating and thus probably don't dream. Of course, your father is not a bear, even if he is increasingly coming to resemble one.

Congratulations on the new job! I'm very happy for you. I would offer to come help with the move, but I don't feel right leaving your father. Do you think you might have time for a short visit before you go? The painters are coming this afternoon, so I don't have time to write more, but I will be in touch soon!

The house looks great! See attached pictures. I'm looking forward to seeing you next weekend. Thank you for making time for us.

It was so nice to see you. I know I give you a hard time about settling down into family life, but I am very proud of all that you've accomplished in your career. I know things are different for your generation. I try my best to keep up. Thank you also for being so understanding about the situation with your father and respecting my wishes with regard to medical intervention.

I think you're right, he does look more bearlike by the day. I know this will sound odd coming from me of all people, but I feel there is some kind of meaningful process happening here with your father, something I dare not disturb.

Good luck with the apartment search! Send me pictures.

During your visit you asked me what I talk about when I'm down in the basement, and at the time I felt too embarrassed to give you a proper response. But now I wonder if it might be good for me to be a little more forthcoming with you. Who else is going to listen to me? And there are so many things I've never said.

When your father and I were first together, he was living in this incredibly awful little apartment in Astoria. It was technically a one bedroom, but the bedroom was basically a glorified closet, just big enough to fit a Queen-sized bed. I liked that place, though. It suited him. My happiest memories of all our years together are from that apartment. And when I was pregnant with you. That was a very happy time, too.

As you know, I've always had trouble sleeping, and your father has always been a champion sleeper. Back then I would lie awake in the blue-black pre-dawn and watch him, and he was so beautiful like that. So peaceful, so vulnerable. So different from how he was in waking life: strong willed, certain. Don't get me wrong, I loved that side of him, too. I've always been attracted to really masculine men. I know that's out of vogue right now, but it was a different time, or I suppose it's just how I am.

Still, it was lovely to see him that way, his face soft and open. I felt like I could see the child he had been and the man he would age into all at once, and I'd imagine our lives together. He was still in grad school, and he'd talk big about the amazing architect he was going to be and how we'd travel all over the world together before settling down to have kids. We had this dream of moving out into the country in our old age, way out into the mountains, and we'd have dogs and chickens and goats and maybe even a horse. Our kids and grandkids would come to visit. There'd be plenty of room, and we'd love all the noise and chaos, but it would also be nice when they left and it was just the two of us again. It was such a beautiful dream.

It's funny how different it all turned out.

Yes, we really did imagine that future together! And yes, it is a contrast to the father you know. It's true that he is not generous with his feelings. Your father has so many good qualities, but an open heart is perhaps not one of them. It's not his fault, or not entirely. He really is a sensitive man, but he wasn't raised by people who knew how to deal with that. You never met your paternal grandparents, but they were hard people. I respected them, but I can't say I ever really warmed to them. You think your father is rigid, but you never met Roger and Berniece. Good Lord. Souls of iron, those two. So of course your father was never really taught how to feel his feelings.

He tried, though. He laughed a lot in those early years, before he started working. It was that first job of his—that's when things really started to shift. The practice of architecture was so different from what he'd imagined. Grueling hours, terrible pay, abusive management. And it was a field where you really had to have connections to get ahead, or else crazy talent, or amazing social skills. Don't get me wrong, your father was a talented draftsman, and he had a wonderful imagination. He had beautiful ideas. But as you know he has never been good with people. So stubborn, so independent, so proud.

He was miserable at work, and he'd come home late—by this point we were married and living together—and there just wouldn't be anything left in him. Physically he was there, but not really. That was hard. I was still so in love with him, and we were married, and suddenly he wasn't there. You think when you're young that you can love someone into being okay, into being the person you believe they can be. It took me a long time to accept that that isn't true.

Anyway, I found some of his old sketches when I was cleaning out upstairs. I saved them for you.

Your father was a real romantic when we were first together. I know that's probably shocking to you, but he was. His apartment building had this wonderful roof. It was terrifying to climb up there—the fire escape was rickety and you know I'm scared of heights—but it had this beautiful view of the whole skyline. We used to have picnics up there in the summers after the sun had gone down and the air was starting to cool. That's where he proposed to me. He didn't make a big fuss with the ring and going down on one knee. He just turned to me one night on the roof and said that if he could share the rest of his life with me, he wouldn't need much more. I said I would like that, and then we made love right there in the open air, the black concrete of the roof still warm under my back. God knows, it wasn't the first time we had sex (I know you think of our generation as great prudes, but we were young once, too) and yet it felt entirely different. I felt like I was coming home to myself. And while I knew that sex could be joyful and silly and angry and beautiful and tender, I think that was the first time I understood it could also be sacred.

Goodness, how sentimental!

I have a confession to make. If I'm going to be totally honest, I think your father really is turning into a bear. Please see the attached photos and tell me what you think.

Thank you for not saying that I've lost my mind. Whatever your father is going through, it does seem to be accelerating. But hear me out—I don't know if it's a bad thing. He looks very peaceful, in a way I haven't seen him look in many years, and I've really been enjoying talking to him. I've been trying to tease out where we went wrong. He took so much upon himself. It was so important, I think, for men of his generation and background to feel like providers, like they had won at the game of work and money and could look after their women. Is that still true for men your age?

I am enjoying having the house to myself again. I love your father, but his constant hovering this last year was too much. It's a relief to be turned loose again. It reminds me of the way I felt after I sent you off to kindergarten. I kept telling you to be brave, but you didn't need that. You ran right into that classroom, making friends practically as soon as you'd entered the door. My brave, bold girl. Where did you get that from? So I guess I was telling myself to be brave then. I didn't feel brave. I had to turn around and dash home so that no one would see me break down.

Once I adjusted, though, once I accepted that my days of having babies were over, that there would be no more babies, there would be only you—and my goodness, if I only got one, I always thought, I'm so glad I got you—once I relaxed into that truth, I started to enjoy having the house to myself. I made new friends. I took up knitting. I started going for long walks on my own. I felt like I finally had time to look at things, to think about things, to settle back into myself. I'm so grateful for that. That was your father's gift to me. He kept working so that I didn't have to go back to work right away, so that I could have that stillness and space after the chaos of your early years, which remain both the best and hardest years of my life.

I can't believe you didn't know I felt that way! Have I really never said that before? I'm sorry. It's true, though. All of it. I guess I've never been great at talking about my feelings either. My family didn't really do that growing up, and while I've tried, it's hard. Your father hasn't helped. I think at a certain point, maybe around the time you left for college, he and I stopped talking. I mean, we still chatted, but we didn't really talk anymore. I don't know why. Maybe too many things piled up unsaid and both of us got scared of our anger, our disappointment. Because my God, that man has let me down, and I have been so angry at him. That's one of the many things that has surprised me about love, how very close it lives to hate. Maybe hate is even necessary to it. Maybe in order to really love someone, you have to be able to hate them sometimes. Maybe it would have been better if we'd let ourselves be angrier with each other, if we'd let ourselves scream and fight and tear at each other until we'd broken ourselves back down to those sweet, soft children. But how would we have known how to do that? How could we have trusted it would work? Neither of us had ever seen anyone tend a long love successfully. No one ever told us that love has its own rhythms, its own lifecycles. I don't think I understood that until I had you.

How did having you change me? Oh gosh, where to even begin! I knew right away when I got pregnant. I don't know how, I just did. I went to the doctor and told him, "I'm pregnant." He was skeptical, but the tests confirmed it. I thought about calling your father at work but then decided to wait until he got home. I wanted to see his face. And I wanted to be alone with you for a little while longer. I went home and took off my dress and sat on the couch in my underwear, a hand on my belly. I just sat there, not even thinking really. Just feeling. Just letting myself settle into this big, new, terrifying love. Because I loved you immediately. Even before I saw your weird, wrinkly little face. (You were not a particularly photogenic infant, as you know.) I loved you because you were part of me but also part of your father, and I loved him so completely that it felt like this was the only way I could truly express the depth of that love. To give him a child. To give myself over to a creature that was both his and mine. But what surprised me as I sat there on the couch that day was that I also loved you for you, for being this unknown little person who would be both of us and entirely different from us. And then after you were born—well, I'm getting ahead of myself.

Your father was so happy when I told him. We were both crying and laughing, and then the laughter passed and we just stood there in the front hall staring at each other with tears running down our faces like we'd just invented the greatest miracle of being human all by ourselves. Which, in a way, we had.

Your father was different during the pregnancy, more like his old self, sweet and tender with me in a way that often moved me to tears. But also, hormones! Everything moved me to tears! I'd weep at the sight of children on the playground or a man petting his dog or a family in a boxed cake commercial on TV. I felt so raw and open to the world. I felt like I had this boundless compassion, like all the borders of me had just dissolved. It was wonderful and awful at the same time.

And then you were born, and if I thought I'd been open before, well, your birth just cracked me right in two. I mean literally. I felt like my whole body was splitting at the seams. Afterward, I kept having these dreams in which there was a big egg in my chest that suddenly cracked open and this viscous, glowing, golden liquid flowed out, filling up my chest cavity. I would sit up at night watching you sleep, which everyone told me was crazy. I mean if your baby is sleeping, you should be sleeping! But I couldn't help myself. It was like everything I had ever known of love in my whole life was just a drop in the bucket. I understood then that love is bigger and stranger and wilder and deeper than any of us will ever know, and that growing up is just the experience of being split open again and again by love and its attendant grief, our hearts expanding each time.

Which is a way of saying that you broke my heart when you were born, and you have been breaking it ever since in the most painful and profound ways. I know you will think it's cliché, but the thing I am proudest of is being your mother, because it is the hardest thing I have ever done—and the best.

I'm sorry I badger you about grandkids. You are right that in some ways it is a selfish wish. I think there are still things I'd like to discover about love, and I think seeing your children come into this world would crack me open again in a way I can't predict. I want that. I think that's one of the ways that women are different from men. We are more willing to let love break and bend and shape us. Men resist that more. I don't know if that's innate or the way we teach them. I feel like men could learn a lot about love from women, in the way that women can learn a lot about strength and power and determination from men. Our love for one another becomes our best teacher, if we let it. Though a lot of men don't. And I hate to say it, but your father has too often been one of those men.

But it's also not a totally selfish wish. I want you to experience the full depth and challenge and beauty of love. It was so good for me. So worthwhile. What could possibly be more worthwhile? But maybe you'll find that kind of love in a different way. I don't know. But I do hope you find it.

I know I alluded to this, but after you were born your father changed again. He hardened again. Became even harder, maybe. More fearful, more rigid. And angry. Of course, it was a stressful time. He had to work long hours and then come home and not sleep well, and I was cranky and blah blah blah. The old story. But there was something else, too. He loved you so much. I could see it. Yet he was so scared of that love. I saw that, too. He didn't let it crack him open. He fought it. And that was not good for him or for you or for us. You can't fight something like that. It's like swimming against a rip current. You just keep at it until you tire and drown. The only way out is to let yourself flow with it until you're back in still water. I don't think your father ever figured that out.

I was telling him that today. I'd never said it to him before. I don't know if I ever really articulated it for myself. But it felt good to say it. I felt something soften in me as I did, and I swear I saw something relax in him as well. So once more I find myself surprised by love, the ever-expanding horizon of it.

I appreciate your saying that. I've sometimes felt that you judge me very harshly, that you judge our marriage a failure. And of course it is! Every marriage is a failure. It is an impossible project. But also—and this is what I've always hoped you'd discover for yourself—there are some faces of love that we are only allowed to glimpse at the end of long patience. Now that we are old and I am sitting here watching the man of my life change into a bear—oh how fucking WEIRD! (I'm sure you'll be shocked that I'm swearing, but if ever there was a time for it!) Anyway, what I am trying to say is that I think I am discovering a new kind of love as I sit and watch over your father in these last days of his transformative rest. It is a love that is close to death, when all the veils are stripped away. If one of the greatest acts of love is to hold someone through their passage into life, then the necessary inverse is to hold someone through their passage into death. Only then are we complete. It is mostly women, I think, who do this, who understand this. It's not that men can't, but that they too often choose not to. They are too often guilty of turning away.

Reading over what I wrote yesterday, I feel a little silly. You are right that I'm not being fair. I love your father. He is a good man. And I am grateful to him, because without him I would never have come to know any of this. He has helped me become myself. What a gift that is.

It's official! Your father is a bear! I heard a bang early this morning and went running down to the basement. But there was your father, slumbering on, the futon having collapsed under his new weight. I did some googling and I think he is a brown bear, which makes sense because those are the bears most common in our region. Supposedly male brown bears wake up in mid-March, so I guess he should be stirring soon.

I placed a bulk order for wild-caught Alaskan salmon and have restocked the deep freeze with all the foods the Internet says brown bears like to eat. I think your father will be hungry after his long sleep. I'll call you as soon as he's up.

I left you a voicemail, but I thought I'd email as well. Your father woke up this morning. I was with him when it happened. One of his legs started twitching, and then his eyes opened, and suddenly he was awake. I looked into those big, brown, animal eyes and I knew that my husband was still in there. "I love you," I said. "I'm so glad you're back." He nodded and gave a little snort, and I felt that maybe he had in fact heard everything I'd said over the winter. I went and put my hand on his head, and he leaned against me. It was a reassuring weight. I told him I'd go get him some salmon, but he just pressed into me a little more, so we stayed like that, still and together, for a while longer.

He's a good roommate! Weird, right? Just like I told you on the phone. He is a very polite and tidy bear. Of course we've had some accidents. He sat on one of the good dining-room chairs and it collapsed, but that's fine. I didn't think the bed frame would support his weight, so I got rid of it and bought a new California-King mattress and put it right on the floor, and that suits us. He is remarkably comforting to curl up next to at night. I feel like a young woman again, like a girl newly in love, who feels that the safest and best place in the world is under her lover's arm. We lie like that for hours, him on his side and my head on his ribcage, as I listen to the strange slow beating of his new bear heart.

For what it's worth, he seems happier than I've seen him in years. I was in the kitchen doing dishes the other day, and I looked out the window and he was there in the yard, sitting on his haunches, watching one of those little cabbage moths flit about, a look of absolute delight on his face. When it flew away he started chasing after it, lumbering but playful. When was the last time I saw that man play? My God. I started smiling, then laughing, then crying, then all three at once. We are so lucky. How rarely one gets another chance.

Who cares what the neighbors think! I cannot believe you of all people are asking me that. Once you've settled in and can take a break from work, you should come visit and see for yourself. No pressure. But it would be nice.

Your father disappeared for a bit today, and I got nervous, though I am trying to trust that he can look after himself. He came back after a couple hours with an entire dripping honeycomb in his mouth. I brought a dish out and he dropped the honeycomb into it, then looked up at me, and while I am still not entirely confident in my ability to read his facial expressions, I would have to say he looked pleased as punch. He had a few stings on his snout, so I made him a cold compress, and then we sat side by side on the back porch. I scooped up the honey with my fingers and took turns feeding it to him and eating it myself.

Yes, you are right. Oddly enough, we are doing very well. I'm so looking forward to your visit. I think we'll have a lovely time. As for the neighbors, it's been a mixed bag. Some of them have been nice about it. People surprise. But not everyone, of course. Your father and I have taken to walking around the neighborhood in the evenings, and Lou Ellen saw us the other day and practically ran screaming into her house. Susie G. gave me a snooty look the first time she saw us, but then she showed up yesterday with muffins and a boatload of questions. She said she was impressed by how content we both seem. How did we do it? I got the sense that she was hoping a similar transformation might overtake Joe. And who knows? Maybe it will prove catching.

I miss you already! I hope you had as nice a time as I did. After you left, I sat on the porch with your father and my knitting and we watched the summer sun slowly sink behind the trees. I know I told you this already, but I'll say it again: I think Los Angeles suits you. You looked healthier and more relaxed than you have in ages. You seem to be settling into yourself in a lovely way. I'm proud of you. And I'm looking forward to meeting your new person when the time is right. No hurry. Maybe your father and I will come out and see you. I'd like to take him to some of the National Parks out West. I'm thinking we could splurge on a nice RV, something big enough for your father. Next summer, maybe. But for now, I'm glad you're happy, and I want you to know that we're happy, too. Write soon with news. I always love hearing from you.

VAL RIGODON

Lipshine #18 Champagne Gold

We could watch the moonrise from the pool, float on our backs, and count the silver spacecrafts puttering across the watercolor sky, striping it with seafoam-colored chemtrails, but you roll your eyes. Your sharp triangle teeth pop black bubblegum, the special promotional kind they stopped making years ago but which I still find littering the bottom of your coat pockets. You shake sand out of your sneakers and break another choker. You've got a dozen replacements downstairs in that scallop shell you stole from your older sister. You jog out of the house: my mauve mermaid girl with feathers on her eyelashes, ears rotten from cheap silver.

You sold your legs to stalk about the sandy shore, to wrap around some devil's red roaring motorcycle. Your band of rowdy angels will be waiting for you at the new-old-revamped-reopened multiplex at the mall, where you loiter after curfew. Everyone wonders how you got your gang to plummet from the pearlescent heavens, to stuff their cotton-soft feet into beat-up sneakers and walk the speckled concrete—but me, I already know.

We were from the deepest, coldest depths of the black-green sea. We were mermaid girls with diamonds in our teeth. You swam around like you owned the place, and maybe you did. But you traded it all away like bottle caps in coral reef. You sold your jellyfish hair that once streamed behind you in luminescent pink and orange, and now you stay shaved, pushing rose thorns from your head. You wanted gravity and feathers and asteroids. I had never imagined the sun; I only wanted to be your shadow. I followed you up here, but I should have known better.

"Kiss me," I begged when we were bending in the wind, scalps exposed to the ultraviolet.

You turned away and stared into your yellow clamshell mirror.

You had a hundred layers of waterproof eyeliner to apply.

"Nah, your breath smells like fish."

Then you ran, already an expert, already the lean-legged king of the forest.

You took my voice with you like a piece of mint floss wrapped around a wiggly tooth and a brassy doorknob. I was always the fool. My breath never bothered you before, but up here in the air you were putting on airs.

Now I sit on your bed while you're gone and wait for you to come home, red hot and sweating and wanting comfort from the unrelenting ground. We don't know how to swim anymore. I try on your gold lipgloss, taste your mouth there, and stamp kisses on the back of my hand. I wrap myself in towels and sit on the roof and let the wind dry my hair until it is a salt-crusted curtain. I stare up at the sky and watch the speedcrafts weave down the nebula highway, dodging stars all by myself. I separate my tail into two long, oak-tan legs and pretend I know what roots are. I pretend that walking is the coolest, chicest thing a mermaid girl can do. And I don't think of the savage sea, where girls like us hunt squids and crash ships and pierce our noses with stolen fishhooks and hide gold in deep, black, hot places and don't wear lipgloss.

Nah, I don't think of those things at all.

ZAK SALIH

The Death of Alexander the Great

When they pass Mr. Nestor's house, Mike asks his parents to turn on WMMS. A boy again, at twenty-one, in the backseat of his parents' car, his own car in the front drive with its broken transmission, asking Mom and Dad to play some music. Through their cigarette smoke, he watches the morning release the Cleveland suburbs from sleep. Cars and buses flash silver on their way downtown. Trees lie wrecked on lawns after last week's storm. A mackerel cat stalks a finch along the eaves of the corner store.

Mike's mother turns the radio on.

"—of 271 American lives lost this week, a stark report that—"

She quickly changes the station.

"—remains had recently arrived in New York City for her funeral, barred to reporters and the public, who nevertheless lined up to pay respects to the woman they said could make even the most rock-hearted man cry."

"So sad," his mother says. She blows smoke out into the morning and starts to whistle "Somewhere Over the Rainbow."

Dead soldiers.

Dead film stars.

No one, on this station or WMMS or any other, says a word about Alexander, as if the brief mention Mike caught on the television news last night, between a segment on his brother and other hometown war heroes and sick elephants at the Metroparks Zoo, had been a mixed signal from another state, another universe. An old woman out for a morning walk in Trumbull Park had found the body left like litter in the meadow. A body later identified as Alexander Rush.

Mike said nothing when he heard the name. He sat on the sofa and sucked his cigarette dry and remembered Alexander's advice. *Never look sad. They won't pay for a crybaby.*

The police mentioned guns, gangs, heroin. Mike's father, high on his oldest son's celebrity, scoffed. A woman held shaking hands to her face, spoke of a son she felt she'd never known, and Mike tried to find Alexander in the gaps between her fingers.

During the weather, the lotto numbers, Mike thought of the cautionary films from high school about what heroin did to a body. The bleary eyes, the needle marks like bug bites, the inexplicable rage and paranoia. But Alexander hadn't been angry or suspicious. His arms had been clean of everything save the scattered moles Mike liked to count when he was too nervous to look into Alexander's eyes.

Alexander had no need for heroin in Trumbull Park.

The other boys, maybe.

But not Alexander.

Breathing in the backdraft of his parents' exhaust, Mike yearns for his own pack of cigarettes, which he's forgotten at home, which he can see on the garish yellow felt of the armchair in his bedroom. Sure, he could bum one of his mother's White Horses or his father's Solents, but Alexander had exclusively smoked Rothmans, which means Mike exclusively smokes Rothmans. To do otherwise, especially this morning, would feel sacrilegious.

Goddamn cigarettes on the goddamn chair, he thinks.

His mother brought the ugly beast home last year from an estate sale. A chair for listening to your music, she had said. Mike had seen right through the gift, of course, all the way down to her desperate desire to keep him safe from the violent world to which she'd handed over George, now off flying his planes somewhere in Southeast Asia. It was broken, too, the chair. The springs had long lost their tension, the weak wood slats on its underside felt ready to snap. Still, the chair wasn't without its use. One evening, when Alexander was a no-show at the school, Mike had come home to his room, turned up WMMS, and pulled the slats out of the chair, one by one, like rotten teeth. Here, under a stack of bath towels, he stored the shoebox that held the money he'd made, his mother's gift an illicit bank for the illicit income he had hoped to one day present to Alexander like an offering before a king.

A gift that didn't say, *Stay.*

A gift that said, *Let's run away together.*

At a quarter to seven, they pull into the family service station. Mike gets out to open the two garage doors, MERRITT stenciled on the left, REPAIRS on the right. His mother and father go to open up the office. In the small employee bathroom, Mike changes into his stained coveralls. He fingers his first name stitched in cursive on a green lozenge like a shield above his heart. *MIKE JR.*

Back in the garage, he tears yesterday off the calendar below the clock, crumples it, and drops it in the bin.

JUN 27 gone.

JUN 28 here.

To avoid thinking about Alexander—alive in his arms, dead in the damp grass—Mike crawls, slowly, carefully, under the belly of last night's half-finished Buick. And there it is: the familiar cave of pipe and grease and dirt, the clank and crank of another day's labor. Mike lubes and scrapes and tightens. He follows his father's directions, works the way his father taught him. The Merritt way. He surfaces every now and then to linger in the breath of the electric fans, to watch his mother soap the finished cars and drive them to the edge of the small lot where they wait, gleaming, for their owners. Then he goes back down.

After he'd seen the news, Mike slipped out of the house and ran to the abandoned elementary school, desperate for anything the reporter wouldn't say, but the other boys had gone by then, scattered like frightened birds. None of them were lovers, he knew. None of them even friends. Not Barry, not Luke, not any of the other spontaneous hustlers. There was something ineffable, or at least impossible to discuss, about their haphazard gatherings, their moonlit parliaments. Still, Mike bristled at their absence, their disrespect to the memory of their now-dead leader.

Hugging the shadows because he had no interest in being seen but also no interest in going back home, not to that house, to that room, to that broken chair, Mike tried to conjure Alexander's ghost. The best he could do was a faint outline, the wavering image of a slender figure peeling like tape from the cafeteria wall and striding forward to teach him the rules of this work, the phrases and sentences and entire conversations Mike could conduct with his eyes, or his hands, or the spread of his legs. Chewing gum to say, *I'll put it in my mouth.* Undone shoelaces to say, *You can hurt me a little.* A fresh cigarette to say, *Follow me.*

"You have to learn the language fast," Alexander told him. "Johns want us young, not wet behind the ears."

"And what do you want?" Mike had dared to ask.

"It doesn't matter," Alexander said.

"Sure, it does."

Alexander flashed his eyes. Mike wanted to flee like a mouse, but suddenly, those eyes softened. They never did that around the other boys.

"You know what I want? To run."

"We could go run laps around the field."

Alexander laughed. "Not far enough."

"How far, then?"

"New York. San Francisco, maybe, but I hate the ocean."

Alexander killed his Rothman and slid to the ground. Mike did the same and watched the toes of Alexander's sandaled feet flex for distant coasts. They huddled together under the lip of the cafeteria roof and shared their last Rothman, Alexander the lord of everything, the master of this strange world, and Mike content to simply sit beside him.

Unlike Mike, who'd been tricking for only three months, Alexander had started his junior year of high school and regaled Mike with stories of the men he'd encountered. Men who cried, men who apologized. Men who displayed, like badges, photos of wives and children in the wallets they opened to pay him. Men who got angry, who gripped the steering wheel and gave it a good Indian burn. Men who hiked up their pants and stalked off without a word, sometimes without even paying. Mike hated those stories. He didn't want to think of Alexander doing the same things he himself occasionally did. He refused to imagine Alexander's beauty cheapened like that.

Across the abandoned school parking lot, a car slowed. Seconds later, it moved along.

"They don't pay for the sex," Alexander told him. "You know that, right? Tell me I've taught you that much. It's the silence that costs. They don't want our mouths open, they want them shut." He passed the cigarette to Mike's eager fingers. "They have no idea who they are, no idea what they want. At least we do."

Mike didn't know what to say to that. What, after all, did he want from this life, from these occasional rebellions against the one his parents had laid before him? Shouldn't he know by now? Or could smoking here with a beautiful boy he hardly knew be enough?

"Just a few more weeks," Alexander said.

"Then what?"

"I'm gone. Out of here." He plucked the cigarette from Mike's fingers and sucked the remaining life from it. "Don't worry. Once I get where I'm going, I'll send you a postcard and you can join me, if you want. We could have a time of it."

I'd like that very much, Mike thought, and was about to say as much when Mr. Nestor's green Pontiac crept up the parking lot, its headlights off. Through the open passenger-side window, Mike heard an oboe, or a trumpet, on the radio.

"Time for music lessons," Alexander said.

He dragged the dead cigarette against the cafeteria wall and slipped into the passenger seat. He turned to blow Mike a kiss; then the car carried him off into the night. Mike climbed to his feet and strolled home through the dark streets, his pockets empty, his heart full.

After Mr. Ellicott's pickup is another Buick in desperate need of oil, so Mike doesn't notice Mr. Nestor's Pontiac until it's halfway up the drive. Through the space between his legs, he watches Mr. Nestor walk up to the office. Sponge-faced, sloppy in a short red tie and baggy blue blazer. Exhausted, like everyone, by the summer heat. He points at his car, and he and Mike's father bend to inspect whatever the problem might be. Mike suspects there is no problem; with Mr. Nestor there usually isn't. Every oil change, brake check, fender polish holds a daytime meaning for Mike's parents and a nighttime meaning for Mike only.

While Mike's father peers inside the wheel well, Mr. Nestor peers at Mike, who picks up a wrench he doesn't need and pretends to worry at something. After a moment, Mr. Nestor and Mike's father walk into the garage. Mike tracks the car mechanic's coal-black work boots, the bank president's tan loafers with their tiny tassels.

"We'll figure it out," Mike's father says. "I'll give you a ride back to the bank."

"Lifesaver," Mr. Nestor says. "Hope it's no trouble. Penny's on call, so I drove myself."

"No trouble at all. We keep the service personal here. I'll be right out."

Mike's father closes the office door behind him. Mike holds his breath. Mr. Nestor's left shoe slips under the car and taps the space by Mike's arm. Of all the parts he's seen, either in bright moonlight or dim car light, Mike has never seen Mr. Nestor's bare feet. He imagines toes like little franks freed from puff-pastry blankets.

"Will you be out tonight?"

Mike stays quiet.

"I need to see you. Nine thirty. Wait for me."

The right cuff of Mr. Nestor's slacks quivers. A crumpled ten-dollar bill drops to the concrete. A loafer nudges it under the car.

"Losing money everywhere." Mr. Nestor chuckles. "What kind of banker am I?"

Mike's father comes out of the office.

"Your chariot awaits, sir."

Loafers turn to follow black boots down the driveway.

"You know we're thinking of your boy," Mike's father says.

"We're thinking of George," says Mr. Nestor.

"Our two warriors."

Mike wants to throw something, anything, to remind his father that he has two sons. Instead, he takes the ten-dollar bill and tucks it into the hip pocket of his overalls—it's the only outburst available to him—and thinks of all the things he's done with his hands and mouth, how his father would gasp at such stories. When he finally gets back to work, he has to take care not to bite off the tip of his tongue.

At noon, Mike takes Mr. Nestor's ten dollars across the street and brings back a sub roll with ham and hot peppers for his mother and a tomato and cheese sandwich for himself. His father, who refuses to eat lunch, satisfies himself with the plastic sacks of oyster crackers in the office. Mike sits on the lawn outside the garage to eat. He eyes the church at the far end of the road and imagines a funeral service for Alexander, thinks of walking through winding ribbons of mourners up to the open casket, of kissing lips gone pale with powder. Not a blown kiss but a real one, a true one. A passionate kiss, with no one to see them but the mosaic Christ with his outstretched arms, attendant to countless sermons, marriages, funerals, but surely nothing as queer as this.

When he's done eating, Mike takes the keys to Mr. Nestor's Pontiac from the office and begins easing the car into the garage. It's impossible not to stare at the empty passenger seat where he has exposed himself for five dollars, made himself come for ten, leaned over into Mr. Nestor's humid lap for twenty. With one hand on the wheel, he opens the glove box and searches for any remnant of Alexander. He rifles through folded street maps, a dog-eared owner's manual, dull pencils, and then he sees it: a crumpled package of Rothmans he fingers like a relic until he nearly scrapes the right-side mirror against the garage door. At the sound of the brakes, his mother looks up and shakes her head at Mike through the glass. Mike's father glares at him from over the hood, a hand out to stop the car in its tracks.

Mike drains the oil from Mr. Nestor's car, watches the thick black rope drop into an old tin pan. He accidentally knocks the pan once, twice, with his elbow, and spent oil creeps like worms out from under the Pontiac. Behind his sweaty right ear, a filched Rothman from the half-empty pack in Mr. Nestor's car goes damp.

Mike is in the office bathroom holding the unsmoked Rothman in his palm when his father returns with Mr. Nestor. Through the hollow door, he hears his mother hand Mr. Nestor a receipt for one hour of labor.

"Couldn't find anything wrong with it, Gene. Runs great. We swapped out the oil for you, though."

"Thanks, Rose."

"Any news from Arnold?"

"No. Penny's a mess. Every day without a letter, she thinks he's dead in the jungle."

"It's awful. We heard from George last week. I still can't listen to the news."

"I told Penny there's nothing to be done about it. Be proud Arnold has the courage for something greater than himself. But I don't need to tell you that. George is doing great things. And life certainly isn't without its risks."

"It certainly is not. Thanks for the business, Gene."

"Sorry to waste your time, Rose."

"Not at all. It's always good to see you outside Saint Agnes."

The office door shuts, and Mike comes out of the bathroom in time to see Mr. Nestor roll into his washed Pontiac at the end of the drive. Mr. Nestor sees him in the rearview. Gives him a thumbs up.

At home, in the shower, Mike does his best to scrub away the stains of the day. He changes into a white T-shirt and jeans. He rolls the sleeves to his shoulders, tucks his damp brown hair under George's red Indians cap.

At the dinner table, they eat reheated beef stew and they smoke. A solemn George ponders them from the framed photograph on the kitchen counter. The shrine, with its tiny American flags in jam jars, like a constant rebuke of Mike's secret life.

Afterward, Mike's parents take their cigarettes into the living room to watch television. Mike goes upstairs, turns on WMMS. He sits on his bed and stares at the mustard-colored armchair. He thinks of George cutting through eastern skies in his American bomber, of Alexander lying blank and lifeless under the trees in Trumbull Park. He takes the Rothman he stole from the pack in Mr. Nestor's glove box and sets it in his plastic ashtray, separate from the other butts.

Mike has been with Mr. Nestor three times.
Once in the alley behind the hardware store.
Once on the side of the road at the edge of town.
Once in one of the elementary school's abandoned classrooms.
He's never smelled cigarettes on Mr. Nestor before.
Back downstairs, he puts on sneakers and heads for the door.
"Walk," he says.
"Careful," says his mother.

There's no one else at the old elementary school. There's only Mike, smoking against the cafeteria wall and staring into the space Alexander used to occupy, right there, against the painted windowsill. The school ruins feel more forgotten than usual. One could almost hear, if one listened closely, the cry and call of kids at recess.

As he waits, Mike recalls that first night when, on a whim, he'd ducked under the barricades to explore the school grounds and found an old basketball by the steps leading up to the field. He took the ball, miraculously inflated, onto the uneven court and started shooting.

He'd gotten no better at the game with age. Chasing an awkward rebound, he started at the sight of the young man leaning against the white wall of the cafeteria, the pale face with its cascade of blond curls. For a moment, Mike felt he was in the presence of a ghost, of some unfortunate student or teacher trapped in the electrical fire that brought the school down in the spring of 1965. But then the young man picked up the ball, tossed it back to Mike, and came towards him across the faded lines of the court.

The young man, very much real, very much alive, pointed at the pack of cigarettes rolled up under Mike's shirt sleeve.

"Have another?"

Mike dug out the pack and pulled his lighter from the hip pocket of his jeans.

"White Horses," the young man said with disappointment.

"My father's brand."

"Well. Beggars and choosers."

Mike watched the fingers, the lips, the cigarette, the smoke. The lips. The lips. The lips.

"Try Rothmans sometime," the young man said and extended his hand. "Alexander."

"Mike."

They took turns throwing the ball at the warped hoop while they smoked. They were terrible at the game, but they were terrible at it together. Alexander threw and caught effortlessly, and to watch it, Mike felt as weightless as he imagined George felt in his cockpit.

It was Alexander who noticed the man on a nearby bench, in a summer suit, watching them play. Alexander looked at Mike and smiled and pretended to miss Mike's toss. The ball rolled across the court toward the man's shoes. Summer Suit picked it up, appraised them in the evening lamplight, and pitched it to Mike.

"Good catch," the man said.

Then it was Mike and the stranger taking shots until Alexander sighed and said he was calling it a night. He waved to Mike and skipped off.

Mike wanted desperately to follow him, but he and the man were still tossing the ball back and forth and it would have been rude to just leave, wouldn't it? So, they kept playing. Mike felt Summer Suit's eyes on his body and wondered if this was the way other men felt when he surveyed theirs discreetly. He kept his eyes on the pale orange ball, the ruddy white backboard.

"I'm terrible at this," Mike said to break the silence. He wasn't sure if he meant basketball or whatever seemed to be unfurling between them, indiscernible, like the opening of a flower.

"You'll make a fine player someday," Summer Suit said. "If you practice."

"It isn't really my thing."

Summer Suit considered this.

"What is your thing?"

Mike tossed the ball and turned so Summer Suit had no choice but to keep it.

I think my thing already left, he thought.

"I should probably get going," Mike said.

"Happy to give you a lift."

"I can walk. It's not far."

"Really, it's no trouble. It's not safe around here after dark."

Summer Suit dropped the ball. Mike watched it roll off the edge of the asphalt court. When he turned back, Summer Suit held out his wallet, made a show of removing two ten-dollar bills. He motioned to a car, a silver Hudson Hornet, at the far end of the parking lot.

Mr. Nestor pulls up to the school, his Pontiac gleaming like a grin. Mike walks up and leans into the orchestral music coming from the open passenger window.

"Mikey," Mr. Nestor says.

They've done this enough that there's no need for the usual gestures, the usual codes, the empty talk about the weather, about borrowing a pen or spare change, about needing a lift across town. The things said and not said.

Mr. Nestor drives them past the supermarket, the Italian bakery, the Howard Johnson, the new Mobil gas station Mike's father prays will go up in flames. Past the secret spots: the low wall behind the florist, the slip of alley across from the Route 28 Diner, the patch of wild grass near an old housing development where a john from western Maryland once laid out a blanket as if he and Mike were on a picnic. Mike smells the wine on Mr. Nestor's breath and waits for the usual move: a palm on the meat of his left thigh, tapping out the rhythm of trumpets or flutes or whatever instruments are on the radio. There is, admittedly, something empowering about all the men who reach for Mike's thigh. He'd felt it even that first awkward half hour with Summer Suit. For a time, nothing is wrong with Mike, with his life.

After the low-lying apartments and the post-war homes, after the eight-block stretch of Black neighborhood Mike's father calls the Nile River, Mr. Nestor parks across the street from a side entrance to Trumbull Park. He stares at the triangular gates ahead, closed for the night. Mike stares at the glove box.

Ask him, he thinks.

Two cars pass in quick succession. Mr. Nestor grips the steering wheel.

Ask him.

Mike clears his throat.

"Can I have a cigarette?"

"Sorry," Mr. Nestor whispers. "I don't smoke."

Mike, suddenly alive with pride at having caught Mr. Nestor in a lie, leans forward and opens the glove box. Everything is still there: the street maps, the owner's manual, the pencils. The crumpled pack of Rothmans. Mike reaches for the cigarettes to show Mr. Nestor, then notices an object that wasn't there before. An empty leather holster, small as a notebook.

Mr. Nestor shifts to face Mike.

He says, "Let's go for a walk."

They step around the gates and into the park, arm in arm, like lovers. They follow the asphalt path around the picnic tables, a thatched hut, the skeleton of a children's playground. They turn away from a sign that reads LAKE .25 and begin marching through a ragged meadow towards the woods.

"If there's one thing I won't tolerate, it's extortion," Mr. Nestor says. He speaks at a rapid clip, as if he himself were terrified of the approaching woods. As if he were the boy in the red cap and not the wolf. "I told him, just because I work at a bank doesn't mean I have fifteen hundred to spare for every boy I give a ride to. This isn't a marriage, I told him. It's business."

The small pistol pushes into Mike's side.

"Stupid," Mr. Nestor continues, as if he's confessing to the priest at Saint Agnes. "There he was, outside my office, asking me for money. Then he's knocking on the goddamn door of my goddamn house, asking Penny if she needs help with the yard! My son off serving his country, and this queer demanding money! He said he wanted to leave and if I didn't help him, he'd do something. Well, God help me, I decided to do something first."

Mike wills his legs to keep pace, terrified of tripping on his feet, of the insistent pressure above his hip, of the ghoulish treeline up ahead.

"So I picked him up one last time," Mr. Nestor says, shaking his head, "and that's when he told me you were in on it."

Mike stops walking and begins to shake. He feels as if someone has taken an ice-cream scoop to his chest. "I need to sit," he says. He tries not to cry.

"No can do, Mikey."

Mr. Nestor prods him onward.

"I'm going to be sick."

"You're not—"

Something snaps under their feet. Mr. Nestor pulls Mike back and holds him still. They look down at the corpse of something small. A blackbird, or a squirrel, or a possum—Mike can't tell in the dark. Whatever it is, it's going nowhere now. Mr. Nestor steps forward to kick the dead animal out of the way—out of the way, like Alexander—and it's as if Mike finally has permission to move, because he reaches for Mr. Nestor's outstretched arm. Their fingers tangle for the trigger. Mr. Nestor slips on thick grass, and Mike can't hold up his weight, so they fall together like bags of trash. Mike's fingers search and squeeze, and there's the sudden clap of thunder, and now Mr. Nestor's rolling off him and scrambling backward.

"Holy," Mr. Nestor says in disbelief.

He slaps at his stomach like it's on fire.

"Holy," he says. "Holy. Holy."

An unexpected force floods Mike's body, a riot that runs smooth and quick through the veins in his neck and his head and his hands and his fingers. A surge of love and hate pumped from his brain or his heart—he can't tell which—but it's there. Maybe it's always been there.

They stand up in the tall grass, Mike and Alexander.

They raise the gun, warm as a baked brick.

They aim for the window of Mr. Nestor's face.

Mike has no idea what time it is. He finds himself by the waterline of Trumbull Lake, waiting for his body to steady itself. When the riot finally leaves him, when he stops sputtering, he pitches the empty revolver into the lake and limps back through the shadows to the park gates. Mr. Nestor's car is still there, parked along the gravel shoulder, oblivious to everything that has happened.

For the second time that day, Mike gets into the driver's seat. He takes the last three Rothmans from the pack in the glove box, and by the time he parks across the street from his parents' house, the third and final Rothman is lit and halfway gone and Mike is picking at spots of blood on his jeans and thinking of the hollowed-out armchair with its shoebox of cash, of empty highways going east and west, of George up in the night sky, free from gravity. He snaps off the radio and rolls down the driver's side window, lets the end of the last Rothman drop into the road verge.

He watches the lingering sparks intently.

He waits, and he waits.

And there, in the dry grass, he thinks he sees a fire start to catch, and he begins to weep. He turns to the empty passenger seat, and through a trick of tears that can't last, Alexander is there, beautiful and alive. Together they wait for the fire to grow hot and fierce, to rise up into a blaze, to illuminate the night, and to cast them forth in search of lands where they can one day live happy, and unvanquishable, forever.

ALYSIA LI YING SAWCHYN

Transfigure/Transform/Transmogrify

An Essay

I dreamt about a castle; I dreamt I *was* a castle. Dreams are funny like that. A thing can look like or be something else entirely. Your pet cat appears before you as an extinct woodland bird, and though you've never owned a pair of binoculars or bought feeder seed, you are absolutely certain of the avian species and are, simultaneously, confident that it *is* your cat. The question *why?* never crosses your sleeping mind. People are funny like that, too.

I say dream, but I mean nightmare. It was recurring. It sent me out of my bed, out from under its soft, pink blanket, out and around the small circle of the house, whimpering from hallway to living room, to dining room, to kitchen, to hallway and living room again.

In this dream, the castle was under invasion. Small arrows were launched against my walls; rocks were hurled over my ramparts. There were so many men, but it was not their assaults that made it a nightmare. The bolts' impacts hardly hurt; the army, though determined, was puny compared to my size. And besides, a castle has defenses. My ramparts were lined with cauldrons of ore, molten and orange-hot. As the army raised its toothpick ladders to scale my sides, my hand was the mechanism that upended the crucibles' contents onto the heads of the soldiers.

As I followed the house's circle, trying to outpace my dream, I dragged my hand over doorknobs, chair rails, countertops to remember that my hand was only my hand. The arrows did not hurt, but this did: I was both the castle and the men. Both stone and flesh; both invaded and invader. The hot, viscous metal took the fat right off my bones.

Dreams, you know?

In a different world (or maybe the same one), a girl sits in a doctor's office with her legs folded up in an oversized leather chair. She looks out the plate-glass window. She looks at the closed soundproof door. The doctor clicks his pen into readiness, clears his throat. His tie has small skeletons playing violins on it.

It would be funnier, she says, pointing, *if you were a surgeon. Something to do more concretely with death.*

His pen moves. *Do you think there's no risk here?*

The girl tries and fails to hide her eye roll. He is unprepared for her, for this, she thinks, despite his wall plaques, his volumes of bound scritta paper, his stately, studded furniture. He thinks it's as simple as separating the obvious from the impossible.

On the doctor's desk is a brass lion, some file folders, and a piece of string—a rope, she thinks—as thick as her ring finger. He sets aside his notes and stands. He shrugs off his jacket. He takes two steps and is suddenly across the room.

Have you done this before? he asks.

The girl imagines she is the brass lion. *Done what?*

Measured yourself, the doctor says.

She blinks, catlike.

He picks the rope up off his desk and lets an end drop to the floor to display its full length. *You see,* he says, *the object is to guess the circumference of any part of your body. How big around do you think your arms are?*

Better than the lion, she is a sphinx.

The doctor will not stop talking.

Your legs? You guess, marking it off on the rope. Then you measure. Compare the difference. You're always smaller than you think.

But she is not smaller than she thinks. She is bigger than he knows. She has grown wings. She has riddles and hunger. She will eat the doctor and pass through the glass window without shattering it and fly away.

I find it confusing, having a body. One night, after I'd gone to bed with too little dinner, my tongue started growing. My teeth folded over under its expansion like they were dispensing paper tickets. It didn't hurt; it was a hallucination.

I mean, it was hunger.

I mean, I thought it might be my actual tongue.

Standing at the front of a windowless, too-cold classroom, I watched the fluorescent lights expand as a student said something about plot or dialogue or setting. A yellow spot with a white center took up half an eye's worth of sight. The spot spread. Class ended. The spot continued to spread as I read further and further down the Google search results for retinal detachment, squinting at my phone screen like a drunk cartoon character. And when the migraine's pain finally came, blasting through my face like napalm, I felt so relieved I couldn't say why I was crying.

What troubles me most is when I feel like I am dissolving and the oxygen/carbon/nitrogen/hydrogen/calcium/whatever of me loosen their bonds. I sink through the bed; I mean, I *feel* I am sinking through the bed. I pass through the mattress and into the carpet before sitting up and shaking my head. It isn't happening, but it *is* happening. I know that beneath the carpet are wooden slats, then cement, then steel, and then earth.

I have never actually been ready to know what it feels like to be in the ground, even though I once thought I was ready to know and sometimes still act like I am.

Let me try to say that again—

No, that's exactly what I meant.

TIMOTHY SCHAFFERT

Dedication

This one's for Mr. XXX in tiny italics
Who knocked at my choppers until I shut up,
the sentiment,
typically tucked in between title and stanza,
is the part of the poem I lick away first,
from the line of your jaw—

and just as quick I put back what I take.
In my tongue's path, tattoos reconfigure,
taking on mouths and voices
to sing their own origin myths.

Cursive up thigh,
lyric lining the spine,
I translate from the French
upon your skin
dirty poems long left un-Englished.

La bite, the slang,
a feminine article for the masculine member,
I translate as *serpent*,
sending it snaking along
the vein of your cock,
a vein likened to a lightning bolt
by a lover of yours I never knew.

And with this noise,
these crashing wrecks,
I arouse the junk-eyed coyotes
and the troops that pilgrim,

death-marching up from miles away
to dance in old storms
and pray to old violence
and worship old punishment,
all the old stories,
once true,
now only fables
in faded ink,
parables revised by their parchment.

JD SCOTT

The Selkie of the City Tells All

We meet at the Mermaid Parade on Coney Island three years in a row. We meet on a rooftop on the Fourth of July, the air smoky with bodega-bought salutes. We meet on a broken-down B3 bus on Avenue U. We meet in front of Macy's between holidays, the arm of an animatronic elf waving in the window display. We meet over dollar pizza. We meet at a concert in an empty pool basin in McCarren Park. We meet in Marble Hill. We meet during intermission. We meet at a rent party. We meet over a rent boy. We meet at a LAN party in Fordham. We meet through the divorce. We meet over hotpot in Flushing, our hands gunning for the same ladle in a tub of sesame sauce. We meet through mutual friends. We meet when the body is discovered. We meet at a rave in an auto-something warehouse beneath the BQE. We meet on DMT. We meet at the Bowery Mission. We meet on the same ferry for forty years. We meet at the Diptyque sample sale: your nose down by a candle, its name spelled in elongated French. You are a classically trained painter who makes do drawing sidewalk signs. You are an electrician with nine fingers. You are on the lam. You are a Slavic Studies major at Columbia. You sell nutcrackers every July at Jacob Riis. You are a piragüero perched up in El Barrio. You make a 524 on your MCAT. You are half-retired, playing dice on the sidewalk in summer, playing a temporary snow laborer in winter. You are a deaf waiter at Tavern on the Green. You read tarot on Grand. You are an absentminded dog walker. You have a stutter. You have the cutest button dimples. You are fighting for your life on Rikers Island. You own a beautiful home in Astoria. You rent a basement beneath a bakery in Sunset Park and break in at night to steal cháng zǐ bāo. You make the best chicken mandi rice in Morris Park. You were born (and will die) in Queens. You are twins who don't know how to share. I remind you of a dentist, of a doorman, of a brother. I remind you of a son, somebody's ex-best friend. We make small talk. I play it shy. I play it tough. I get real sweet when we get close enough.

Then I take my skin off. I am the city, and my skin is cigarette butts and piss-summer scent. It's the same magazine sample of Santal 33 from Le Labo coated onto my pulse. My skin is neon and concrete and sakura blossoming at the Brooklyn Botanic Garden each May. My skin is high rise with all the lights on. It's Times Square. It's *this is a Howard Beach bound A train, the next stop is Broadway Junction.* It's a warm cup of broth in a blizzard, a margarita in a Styrofoam to-go cup in June. My skin is sweat. My hair is kinky, slick, tight, loose, long, buzzed, gone. When you see me, you see the part you need. That's when I stop being the city and become something you can perceive. That's when I grow hands and knees. You see the twenty-three-minute affair at the Christopher Street's westside piers. You see me for twenty-three years in your bedroom. When I take off my skin, you feel comforted. Most of you end up loving me. Sometimes I love you back. Always you see me until our end. Rarely do you see me until *your* end. It never gets easier, that part. I cannot give you eternity. I change for you, sure, but I change for myself, too. I compromise; I make amends. When I fold my skin like a coat in your closet, I become the only knowable part of me. When I give up my secret, it seldom goes well. Inevitably, you start plotting to keep me. You hide my skin away. You decide you can love me best if I cannot be free. You hide it by night. You hide it in the meat freezer. You hide it in a carved-out book. You hide it behind a pipe. You hide it in the only-for-storage oven, along with your birth certificate and tax forms. You hide it like a birthright. You hide it under a floorboard, in the medicine cabinet, inside the sock drawer. I don't like being a kept man, but I'm used to the rhythm, the point where the human heart settles on custody. That's when I get melancholy. I miss operas off-Broadway and lox on bialy. I miss the rats crawling for crumbs on the subway tracks. I miss ignoring celebrities. I miss dim sum and honey locust trees and the view from the top of the Wonder Wheel. I miss early morning surfers at Rockaway. I miss the siren song of the Mister Softee truck. I miss eight million hearts beating all at once. I miss it so hard it calls me back to form. I find my skin. Consider it chipped, GPS-tracked. I always know how to get my skin back. Then I'm a hand on the handle; then I'm no more hands. I'm the ex-boyfriend, the ex-partner, the ex-husband. I'm every diner plate of disco fries, every schmear of cream cheese. I'm every person who has ever felt lonely. I'm every evening commute. I'm every rent freeze. I am a manifestation of your incorporated municipality. I'll be here as long as you are. I exist because you do. I live up in the smoke and the smog; then I come down. I descend. I introduce myself and give you that look. We make small talk and swap rehearsed pitches about jobs. Business cards. Rent hikes. Street guitars. Eventually you lean in. Then—and only then—do I take my skin off again.

PRESTON SMITH

Narcissus Buys a Waterbed to Sleep with Himself

If you feel you're being watched, you are
not alone. I go to bed early, bedraggled
by what the day has wrought, by beauty
and the way Narcissus scorned that lake
with a single look. I never wanted more
than to be water and to manipulate
my shape to the wills of others,
to lie under him just one time.

ADDIE TSAI

Deep Sea Baby, I Follow You

You cannot tell them. You cannot tell your five divine sisters, each as perfectly beautiful as the one before. You cannot tell your grandmother, whose heart would sink to the sea floor like a strange and unwanted anchor. You cannot tell your father, who has relied on you to be exactly as he has carved you to be, the image of his beloved who now resides in Heaven. You cannot tell any of them that who you are in your heart is not who stands before them in their eyes. If only you could throw away your singing voice, spun by the gold of angels. Or so they say. If only you could throw away the curve etched into the torso above your waist and the one submerged beneath, its own wave. But you know more than most the insistence of the waves of "nature." So instead, you finger the shipwrecked statue of that fair, dark-haired prince—not out of a desire for him, but out of a desire *of* him. Okay, yes, maybe also a desire *for* him. You imagine your voice like the belly of a conch shell, your wavy middle like the straight line of the horizon, your hair the swollen bubble a human exhales to live. One day, you draw your fantasy in the sand, and then wipe it away with your tail. Just long enough to feel it become real. At the peak of longing, there she is, the one you should not trust, but the only one who can grant you the desire that burns in your chest like a bright orange fire that refuses to sink. She promises you everything you could ever want: a voice dark and deep as the underground, a face chiseled like stone, thighs as thick as the tree trunks above, a broad chest and a torso as straight as a windowpane, a neck free of the long hair that so many of your kind long for. But, you know the story. Each spell comes with a price. She will give you even your prince, and as it so happens, your prince will desire you in equal measure, but you will have no sex from which to enact your longing. Between your legs will be an emptiness. But who cares about that when you get to return to whom you were always meant to be? You drink the vile potion. Around your neck you wear a simple fish's tail pendant. Your new love fingers it from time to time, which sends a strange chill up your spine—both from desire and a memory that tingles to hold. Not always in a good way. Air is delicious above ground, between kisses. Your prince knows your story, and you both make do with the constraints. You keep the pendant as a reminder of your past life, your family, all you gave up. Of all you left behind in order to become.

MICHAEL VARGAS

The Magician wears a tilma

Sometimes I want what Diego had,
or at least
what all the artists, ethnoarcheologists, and clairvoyants
said
a shawl too drab for possession
but worthless enough to be mistaken as a medium
to distill the holy from the celestial
rapturing of petals bloomed with a garb tied to one's neck like a noose

but much like ancient aliens
as seen on TV
dedicated theories converge at native ineptness
and leave Diego, much like myself, to hang above this hill of violets
and gallica roses

peasant boy talks to eagles up on that hill
wind-burned vestiges
drip organic copper paint off his feathered tail

I forget, much like he knew,
how to smelt blood into cerulean paste
pour every crest of a sepal's backing into silver and gold
manipulate planetary conjunctions
under the dim-lit reflection of a moon's waning nail
only to be discredited as a degenerate renaissance painting

We burrow our bodies in a dream's impasse
constructed of ambiguous cultural remains
capable of withstanding bodily inertia
like the serpent returning to dirt

only to rise on the third day,
enamored behind stone

There is no resounding pontification that can describe our amnesia
no canonization supported by a tilma covered in bullet-proof glass
no church to pay for your sins by way of a barefooted pilgrimage
only an underground nest, much like a cenote,
where snakes with feathers brumate like their warm-blooded siblings
advised thereafter to show men
how to construct temples and burn theirs down with roses

JAE TOWLE VIEIRA

A Figure of Heroic Size

In Katie's hometown—Auburn, California—the scales have been missing from the Ladies of Justice at the courthouse for more than one hundred years. Each of the three statues presides over a cardinal direction. None blindfolded, but none with pupils. All grip modest swords in their right hands, and all their lefts are extended as if to hand back change. Katie's aged uncle wrote an article about the missing scales for the local paper as part of a retrospective in celebration of the new millennium. There are no pictures of the courthouse under construction (one of at least five local mysteries), but photographs of the completed structure from 1897 confirmed that every Iustitia and/or Themis once held a balanced set of scales, swinging on a real chain. The readership appreciated this nugget of local trivia, but no one advocated to reinstate the scales. Their absence had become a tradition of its own.

At conception, back in the late 1800s, reports say the courthouse's dome was capped by "a figure of Progress, of heroic size"—apparently some sort of Cupid, though again there are no pictures—but this Eros was quickly supplanted by a weathervane, which more effectively secured the loyalties of the town. The weathervane was temporarily replaced by the Stars and Stripes during the nationalist fervor of 1917, but this change was received with displeasure. The traditionalists loved Old Glory as much as anyone, but let's not forget that we have a particular way of doing things around here. The weathervane was eventually restored to its place of honor. Patriotism is important in this old Gold Rush town—certainly one of the top five local values—but not so important as history.

Katie's ex-husband has five sons with his new wife, and all of them, from six to sixteen, race dirtbikes. They can be found at the track every Friday night, zipped into black leather suits with fox head logos across the shoulders, revving, helmets glossy even though the stands and the crowd and the cars and the grills and the beams of the floodlights and the railroad tracks and the ponderosa pines are all suffused in ochre dust. The six-year-old is a crowd favorite. Katie knows this because she is one of the photographers who comes to every race all summer long. She takes pictures of the racers in hopes of future sales. This is not as easy as it used to be (and it was never easy, strictly speaking), but it is not impossible to make a living this way. She also photographs monster truck rallies, cross-country ski meets, and the Western States Endurance Run, which is her favorite. She takes portraits of seniors at three local high schools, covers festivals including Railroad Days, the Gold Country Fair, the Placer Farm and Barn Tour, the Mountain Mandarin Festival, Lake Tahoe's Concours d'Elegance, and, with the help of her assistant Ophelia, she shoots weddings. One might say she gets around.

"Kitty," her ex-husband says, leaning against his bike one Fast Friday, cocking his helmeted head. "How've you been? We missed you at Peter's birthday last weekend. The big One-Oh!"

"Double digits," she says, nodding, because Peter is standing nearby, half a hot dog in hand and half in mouth. His helmet, twice as large as his blond buzzed head, is tucked under his other arm. "That's a big deal!" She makes as if to keep walking.

"Really though, how are you?" her ex-husband asks. His voice is muffled; he hasn't removed his helmet. He always holds himself completely still while talking. Katie believes this is because he cannot stand auditory clutter. When they first moved in together, he convinced her to pawn her father's mantel clock. "Ticking is for classrooms and other prisons," he said. The first time they fucked in her bed, he'd attempted to rise above the provocation of her percale sheets. Finally, red-faced and flaccid, he'd asked, "Can't you do something about this?"

"You know me," Katie says.

He waits for her to ask him how he's been. She knows he knows she's heard about his cousin's search for a wedding photographer. She knows he wants to say he'll put in a good word. One wedding can cover up to three months' rent, depending on the depth of the happy couple's pockets and the extravagance of their vision. She should know better than to cast aspersions on potential customers—she should know better than to impose her cynicism on other unions—but she and her ex and his cousin all know they'll never be her customers. No potential.

"Is that John Paul?" she asks. Her ex-husband's head swivels, and she leaves.

"It isn't," he calls after her, and then he says, "Kitty!" but she doesn't turn.

Perched on a fence thirty yards away, Ophelia scuffs her Chucks against a crossbar. She's been watching her part-time boss. She's here with some friends from high school, other kids who stayed local, who've been local all their lives, other kids who know her real name is Leah, other kids who've been forced by love or money or bad grades into stints at the local community college or Taco Tree or In-N-Out, other kids who aren't yet twenty-one, other kids with medical marijuana prescriptions for insomnia or menstrual cramps or ADHD, with Nalgene bottles full of cranberry juice and vodka, with hemp chokers and sunburned shoulders, with damp bikinis underneath denim shorts from a long afternoon picking blackberries and wild fennel down by the river. One of them is wearing her mother's replica *Survivor* buff as a top. It's a good joke; she's so thin. Ophelia texts her half-sister instead of texting Katie. She bites the inside of her cheek instead of letting herself think, Why him?

The answer, as is tradition: at the time Katie was using the wrong lens.

Three years ago, Katie interviewed Ophelia for the assistant position during the Freeride World Qualifiers in Olympic Valley. Katie, never having worked much with other people, found a way of asking her questions without having to ask them. Consequently, do you have your own equipment and do you have a car became meet me in Truckee and be ready to shoot. There was no point forcing applicants—doubtless young, doubtless untrained—to cobble together clumsy portfolios when half an hour's work would tell her what she needed to know.

"I thought you wanted someone to help with weddings," Ophelia had said, shifting her weight in fleece leggings and a maroon anorak.

"Same difference," said Katie, adjusting her fingerless gloves. "It's all timing and light."

Katie was aware that her manner compensated for her uncertainty; she was aware that her brusque tactics were often successful. She did not want people to ask her questions. In Katie's opinion, respect began with the self. Though self-respect didn't guarantee that others would treat you well, to lack self-respect often precluded the possibility. Katie had made the necessary changes slowly, over decades. Progress had been hard won—she was all too conscious of her failings. But she did not know that to Ophelia she represented a mesmerizing indifference to external stimuli. There would be no undeserved nods or smiles, no unearned laughter or eye contact. Ophelia watched Katie listen, recognized that Katie would meet her exactly halfway and no further—and this in contrast to Ophelia's grandmother, bobbing on the stoop before the Mormons in their suits: Hello there, why sure, do come in. Ophelia fell in love with Katie because she knew she would have to earn it. When Katie said—the two of them hovering over the view-screen forty-five minutes later on the day of the trial session, hands cupped to protect the camera from the falling snow—"That's a good one," warmth like sunlit sand had pulsed through her every artery. Of course there was no hope—Katie will always be pragmatic and somewhat monkish to boot—but when has that kind of knowledge ever saved someone a pining?

In ninth grade, alongside all the other freshmen, Ophelia took health class. In health class, they learned about the food pyramid and lactic acid. They learned about Tylenol versus aspirin, polio and penicillin, the efficacy of surgical masks. During the unit in which their textbook ventured south of the belly button, they had a guest speaker: six-foot-four with taut biceps and tattoos on every finger. He tossed a chair across the room while the teacher, old coach Mellon, yawned in a corner. (Unbeknownst to the class, the tossing of the chair happened every year.) He told the class that girls were princesses and should treat themselves as such. He told the class that boys needed to learn self-control lest they end up like him. At the end of the hour, old coach Mellon passed out white cards for the students to sign. I understand that saving sex for marriage is the best choice for physical and emotional health. I hereby commit myself to abstain from sexual activity until I enter a faithful marriage relationship.

Name: Leah Hill.

Date: September 25, 2006.

Ophelia's grandmother was not a Mormon but avowedly a Christian woman, though lapsed from practice. A year after taking health class, Ophelia told her grandmother she was gay. A year after that, Ophelia's grandmother joined sixty percent of Placer County's residents in voting Yes on Prop 8: Eliminate Gay Marriage. Although Ophelia had been confident that Prop 8 would be overturned, although in a few years it would be overturned, although the court's eventual ruling would be one of the gadflies behind Ophelia's decision to make a move with Katie one fateful summer Friday, Ophelia and her grandmother had argued about Prop 8 across the kitchen table—argued in the way Ophelia would not argue during a debate on Gay Marriage in AP US History (six juniors on one side of the room, nineteen on the other), which the valedictorian-to-be would "win" by proclaiming "You can't put a socket in a socket!" to laughter and applause. Ophelia had argued and Grams had deflected until finally she'd condescended to answer, "You can't ask me not to counsel with my heart."

On the Friday Ophelia finally confesses her love to Katie, Michael Landon Wright III is born to proud parents in Sutter Auburn Faith Hospital. They'd meant to birth him in a state-of-the-art maternity ward farther down the hill, but—just like his father—this little tyke moves through life on his own time. At a local high school, administrators are having the janitor repurpose the darkroom: there's no longer such a thing as a negative. Someone is losing her virginity on the hood of a car. Beneath Interstate 80, half a mile from the courthouse, in a drainage passage known by the youth of Placer County as the art tunnel (or Satan's Tunnel) because every square inch is graffiti on graffiti, someone uses a can of spray paint to write a letter to the Universe in the form of a silhouette she has practiced hundreds of times in the margins.

The Western States Endurance Run is considered particularly grueling, owing to altitude and terrain. A photograph: two men in the foreground, one trailing behind, all in neon shorts, all sweating, one bare chested, dull white shoes kicking up dust on the packed-earth track, six inches of snow scowling from the shadows cast by the dark Sierra pines. A photograph: four men and one woman running along a dirt road beside a black lake, snowy peaks looming in the background beneath a bright June sky. A photograph: a line of runners ascending toward the camera in the dim light of sunrise. The Foresthill Bridge arching thin in the background. A path wending through tall manzanita. Snow deeper than a man with a child on his shoulders. No Hands Bridge. Quality dates the images more effectively than the runners or their garb.

At one hundred point two miles, the trail links Olympic Valley to Placer High in the heart of Auburn in the heart of Placer County. Thirty hours is the limit; completion under thirty hours earns you a bronze belt buckle. Times under twenty-four earn a silver. Records and a Wikipedia page immortalize Gordy, Ken, Andy, Andy, Mike, Mike, Jim H., Jim K., Jim H., Jim K., Jim K., Chuck, Herb, Brian, Mark, Tom, Tom, Tim, Tom, Tim, Tim, Tim, Mike, Tim, Scott, Scott, Scott, Scott, Scott, Scott, Scott, Graham, Hal, [year of the fires], Hal, Geoff, Kilian, Timothy, Timothy, Rob, Rob. Katie photographs the women when she can, but pictures of the men traditionally sell better and she can't be everywhere at once. She has encouraged Ophelia to focus on the women, when she can.

Katie undresses slowly in her bathroom, alone. She sees herself newly, and her skin is tender to the touch. She remembers glimpses of her own mother naked a long time ago. That crescent above the mons, those mottled thighs, pubic hair coiling thickly, visible in relief through shifts. Katie pulls a shift over her own head, looks down at the blue of the veins in her breasts. There is one high window she leaves open from March until October. Sometimes it is nice to be cold. There was a time, five years back, when the walls of her apartment were hung with her own prints, but now the walls are bare and she feels she has only just begun to breathe. A pleasure inherent to paring down.

Ophelia remembers sitting cross-legged at the laundromat, four-five-six-seven-eight years old, sitting against the wall, sitting atop a dryer and getting chewed out by the manager, sitting on the broad wooden shelf up among the clothes her mother and grandmother were folding, the slacks and blouses and shifts, staring at the mural on the wall, fifteen feet long and ten feet high, a burnt-out shell of a cabin by a stream in autumn woodlands. "Life-size," she would say, standing to trace the edges of the orange-yellow leaves with her fingertips, and her mother, pale and metastasizing somewhere in the organs, would say, "No, silly girl, you're too big, don't you see?" It was Ophelia's job to match socks.

Ophelia will sit behind you and run her fingers through your hair, combing it all the way through to the tips, pulling it back from your ears to set your scalp tingling, and breathe on your neck. Here? Like that?

A skipping of her fingertips down your arms, moving in warmly to cup your waist when you turn for a kiss deep enough to leave you almost horizontal. She'll press you down. I love the way you smell. A tracery of buttons and clothing folded back. She'll graze you lightly. She'll breathe on your panties before she pulls them down. She'll kiss you through the panties before she pulls them down with her teeth. Warm palms along your thighs, leaving you lifting yourself in response, in offering insistence, tracing hot-wet and kissing away your gasp. Her fingers slide into you, her fingers keep a close distance and pad hinting around your clit, silking the hot swollen lips. Yes? She stops and you murmur. She grins in the dark as she smooths the line of your chin and the hollow of your neck and kisses down. She wants to give; it's how she was raised. She lets you suck yourself from her fingers, her tongue, her lips.

What am I doing wrong? And why don't you want me?

Ophelia lies in the dark, stung and snapped back, as if she'd gotten to touch, as if she'd gotten to try.

Contributor Notes & Artist Statements

SHASTRI AKELLA's debut novel, *The Sea Elephants*, is forthcoming from Flatiron Books in July 2023.

I recently endured a homophobic attack in Hyderabad, my hometown. In "The Magic Bangle," I reinvent Hyderabad's old district as a queer utopia. This decision was inspired by the myths my maternal grandmother once told me. In the South Asia of her tales, nonhumans and humans were equals, wish-granting djinns didn't demand sacrifices, and god was a friend whose blue face you could playfully smear with mud. The telling of such fairy tales, I believe, isn't escapist; it's a way of wishing a desired future into being, of believing that "another world is not only possible, she's on her way. On a quiet day, I can hear her breathing." (Arundhati Roy)

MARY ANGELINO's publications include *The Arkansas International*, *The Southern Review*, *Foglifter*, *Rattle*, *The Cincinnati Review*, and *The Southern Humanities Review*, with work forthcoming in *The New York Quarterly*'s anthology *Without a Doubt*. She has been nominated for a Pushcart Prize and received an honorable mention for the 2019 Auburn Witness Poetry Prize. Her poetry has been anthologized in *Best New Poets*. She lives in Valencia, California, where she teaches composition and creative writing at College of the Canyons and serves on the Santa Clarita Art Council's Sidewalk Poetry Project.

Fairy tales were my first experience with the image. They taught me to see things in my mind's eye: the Beast's blood-red roses, Sleeping Beauty's thorn-choked tower, the gnarled hand of the witch holding out the apple. In "Dear Girlhood" (a love letter of sorts), I let the images from my childhood haunt and pout and sing, tangle and untangle themselves through their forms—anagrams, pantoums, and the mirror poem.

CLAYTON BRADSHAW is a queer, formerly homeless veteran who was a finalist for the 2021 Kinder-Crump Award for Short Fiction. He holds an MFA in Creative Writing from Texas State University and is currently working on a PhD at the University of Southern Mississippi. He is an alum of the Tin House Winter Workshop, and his work can be found in or is forthcoming from *F(r)iction*; *Green Mountains Review*; *Barren Magazine*; *War, Literature, and the Arts*; and elsewhere.

Fairy tales allow us to imagine entities the real world struggles with before accepting them into society. In this way, fairy tales are inherently queer spaces where we may explore our own interiority and birth our authenticity into this world. In "The Ungrateful Dead," I wanted to represent the very real queer struggles of existing in an often hostile world and to show progress within the battle to achieve our ever after.

ROBERT CARR is the author of three collections of poetry: *Amaranth* (Indolent Books 2016), *The Unbuttoned Eye* (3: A Taos Press 2019), and *The Heavy of Human Clouds*, forthcoming from 3: A Taos Press. A seven-time Pushcart Prize nominee, Robert's poems appear in numerous journals and anthologies..Selected by the Maine Writers and Publishers Alliance, he was the recipient of a 2022 artist residency at Monson Arts.

At the nadir of the global AIDS pandemic, I worked full-time in infectious disease response. In my desk drawer at the Massachusetts Department of Public Health, I had one book. Not a clinical text or a strategic plan, but *The Complete Works of Lewis Carroll*. Through Alice's adventures in Wonderland, I found relief from the rabbit hole of premature death. "At the Hatter's Table" revisits the queer erotic in the context of my personal and professional history.

ANNA GRAEME is a queer poet living in Ohio. She received an MFA in creative writing from Bowling Green State University. Their writing explores the spaces between myth, the natural world, and character-driven narratives. Her work has been featured in journals such as *Pleiades*, *Southern Indiana Review*, and others.

Much of my work revolves around mythos. I consider these tales to be wondrous, ever-shifting amalgamations of a tool that was at one point used to explain both the world around us as well as the worlds within us.

HANNAH GRIECO is a writer living in Washington, DC.

I write about the mothers and stepmothers in fairy tales a lot. I love exploring the literary "bad mother" role and how it is shaped by (and even shapes) society's shifting view of motherhood. But in "If you were red riding hood," I wanted to reimagine the character of Red Riding Hood, to examine how she's locked into her own caregiving role, and to subvert the idea of the villain in the story. I wanted to remove all traces of the "bad guy" from this story and instead intertwine female desire and freedom. It felt particularly timely.

ALLEGRA HYDE is the author of the novel *Eleutheria* and the story collection *Of This New World,* which won the John Simmons Short Fiction Award. Her second collection, *The Last Catastrophe*, will be published by Vintage Books in March 2023.

I'm obsessed with the way fairy tales are fertile spaces for literary invention while also serving as conduits for timeless human truths. In "A Whale Tale," I merge a contemporary consequence of climate change with enduring human dramas of love and betrayal. These elements are bound together by the alchemy of fairy-tale magic, which, though fictional, hopefully conveys a sense of meaning, if not the spark of real-world recognition.

CATHERINE KIM is a transgender Korean Canadian writer studying in the United States. Her writing has been published or is forthcoming in *Black Warrior Review*, *Nat. Brut*, *Hypocrite Reader*, Lethe Press's *Transcendent* series, and elsewhere. Her work has been awarded the Frances Mason Harris '26 Prize, shortlisted for the Sunburst Award, and nominated for the Pushcart Prize. She earned an MFA at Brown University and is currently a PhD student at the University of Denver.

"The Fox Marble" draws from Korean folktales about fox spirits, or kumiho. These stories are cautionary tales, chiding the young student to consider heavenly matters and warning fathers against valuing daughters over sons. Sensuous monsters that assume a human guise to prey on human flesh, the kumiho may redeem themselves and become permanently human by restraining their hunger. In "The Fox Marble," braver possibilities unfold as Yeou reimagines her desires and indulges in forbidden fruits.

KYLE MARBUT lives in Virginia. They wrote two chapbooks called *Dawn Chorus Fascicle* and *Ecliptic Tongues.* They have one more secret to tell.

I dropped a mirror and reflected in the shards I split into a hundred eyes, and through them I saw that other world where my mother married a tree and birds could whisper facts and the grave was a door the rain walked through, and I knew it was all true there. That was before I had teeth. Now I only write about real life.

Like Sharon Stone and the zipper, MIKE McCLELLAND is originally from Meadville, Pennsylvania. He has lived on five continents, but now resides in Illinois with his husband, two sons, and a menagerie of rescue dogs. He is the author of the short fiction collection *Gay Zoo Day*, and his writing has appeared in *The New York Times*, *WIRED*, *Boston Review*, *Vox*, *The Baffler*, and a number of literary magazines and anthologies. He teaches creative writing at Eastern Illinois University.

My hometown of Meadville, Pennsylvania, has always been like something out of a fairy tale. You can find it in the middle of a forest, but it's more gingerbread house than Prince Charming. I've resisted writing about home because I have such mixed feelings towards the place where I spent my first twenty-three years. It is a place of great beauty and warm memories, but like many fairy tales, all of the good is shadowed by horror. When I think of Meadville, I think of being bullied, specifically for being gay. Pithole is a stand-in for the town I grew up in, and by weaving the magical and the horrible, I was finally able to visit my hometown on the page. I was able to celebrate some of its wonders and take a little revenge.

CHRISTOPHER NELSON is the author of *Blood Aria* (University of Wisconsin Press 2021) and three chapbooks, including *Blue House*, which earned him a Poetry Society of America National Chapbook Fellowship. He is the founder and editor of Green Linden Press and the journal *Under a Warm Green Linden*.

In tracing the word "fairy" backward through time, we find that it has for centuries suggested the possibility that the world that meets the eye isn't the whole world, that beneath the apparent there is the Other: other truths, other beings, other stories. Go back far enough and this inherent strangeness, this Other, becomes synonymous with the very act of speaking, as if the first and ultimate Other wasn't God or death but the very self we know yet don't exactly know. In writing, I try to keep this mystery close, to let it guide the pen.

REUBEN GELLEY NEWMAN is a writer and musician based in Brooklyn, New York. His poems have appeared in *diode*, *The Journal*, *Variant Lit*, and *Alien Magazine*. He is an editor at *The Adroit Journal* and *Couplet Poetry*.

Over the years, poems have become fairy houses of sorts for my queerness. In "Dear Dear," I'm riffing on Anne Carson's *Autobiography of Red*, where Geryon, the protagonist, has red wings and an aching teenage desire for Herakles. When I wrote this poem, I was living alone in western Massachusetts. I worked in a library and roamed the woods. I pondered fairies and "The Dragon at the Bottom," a poem by my friend Evan Williams. I am less alone in New York City, but I'm writing more about myth through a contemporary lens. Through camp humor and aural rhythm, I'm exploring how fairy tales warp time, history, and desire.

CAROLYN OLIVER is the author of *Inside the Storm I Want to Touch the Tremble* (University of Utah Press 2022), which won the Agha Shahid Ali Prize in Poetry. Her poems have appeared in three chapbooks and in *The Massachusetts Review*, *Copper Nickel*, *Smartish Pace*, *Shenandoah*, *Beloit Poetry Journal*, *32 Poems*, *Southern Indiana Review*, *Cherry Tree*, *Plume*, *DIALOGIST*, and elsewhere. She lives with her family in Massachusetts.

When I return to the fairy tales and myths I knew as a child, I tend to focus—and this is likely linked to the time I spent closeted—on the work of revelation and concealment. Who might be hiding at the story's periphery? Whose outward openness is a mask? Who needs a lift to another time or place to give a fuller accounting of desire, danger, agency?

CAT POWELL is a writer and teacher. She holds an MFA from Columbia University, and her short fiction has appeared in *The Missouri Review*, *The South Dakota Review*, and *Action, Spectacle!* She is working on a novel and is represented by Janklow & Nesbit.

I inherited *The Tall Book of Fairy Tales* from my mother. It was, as promised, tall and narrow and filled with illustrated stories that were closer to their Grimm ancestors than their Disney descendants. The illustration I liked best was of a bear, a cottage, and a red-and-white rose bush, because we had a similar rose situation in our yard. In the story, the sisters Snow White and Rose Red rescue a bear and nurse him back to health in their kitchen. I loved the pet bear, but then he had the gall to turn into a prince with a brother, the ending both inevitable and disappointing.

VAL RIGODON is a creative writer and attorney. She was a 2019 Poets House Emerging Poets Fellow and a storyteller for The Moth. You can find more of her work on the Internet and, someday, in a bookstore. She one day hopes to live in a house by the sea.

I have loved fairy tales ever since I was a young child. I especially sought out revisions and retellings. My favorite stories to write and read include whimsy, magic, and love. I've never been able to resist adding a touch of magic to everything I write.

ZAK SALIH is the author of the novel *Let's Get Back to the Party*. His fiction has appeared in *Epiphany*, *Foglifter*, *Crazyhorse*, *The Florida Review*, *The Rumpus*, and other publications. He lives in Washington, DC.

It's the wilderness in fairy tales that always gets me. The shaded forest where grandmother's house sits, the byzantine caves where dragons rest, the mist-covered mountains where knights seek adventure. There's the thrill of danger, yes, but also the otherworldliness of it all. In fairy tales, you never come out of the wilderness the same as you entered it. You come out transformed. (If you come out at all.) Though perhaps there's something else that's always endeared me to fairy tales, something I had to wait for adulthood to recognize. All those outcasts, spurned by families and society, found themselves in a wilderness where they had to rely on the wisdom of strangers, face their fears, and learn how to survive. That sounds pretty queer to me.

ALYSIA LI YING SAWCHYN is the author of the collection *A Fish Growing Lungs*, which was a finalist for The Believer Book Award in nonfiction. She has received fellowships from the Sewanee Writers' Conference and the Kenyon Review Writing Workshop, and her work has appeared in *Fourth Genre*, *Brevity*, and other publications. She is Editor-in-Chief of *The Rumpus* and a professor of creative writing at Warren Wilson College.

I cannot remember a time in my life before fairy tales. My mother collected children's books, and gorgeously illustrated stories loom large in my childhood memories. I have always simultaneously wished and feared that magic might be real—always looking for strange coincidences, always worried my mind was getting away from me—and as primarily a nonfiction writer, this has produced endless amounts of inspiration and terror.

TIMOTHY SCHAFFERT is the author of six novels, most recently *The Perfume Thief*, which was a Los Angeles Times Top Ten Best Books of the Summer in 2021 and a One World, One Book selection by Penguin Random House International. His seventh novel, a story with ghosts in it, is forthcoming from Doubleday. His work on fairy tales has appeared in the magazine *Enchanted Living* and in the anthologies *My Mother She Killed Me, My Father He Ate Me*; *Brothers & Beasts: An Anthology of Men on Fairy Tales*; and *The Mermaid Handbook*, among others.

Even little snippets of reflection like this can sometimes feel too reliant on reality, and I struggle. Fairy tales, and the portal into imagination and invention the tradition allows, has for many years left me blissfully untethered.

JD SCOTT is the author of the story collection *Moonflower, Nightshade, All the Hours of the Day* (Lake Forest College Press 2020) and the poetry collection *Mask for Mask* (New Rivers Press 2021). Scott's writing has appeared in *Best Experimental Writing, Best New Poets, Denver Quarterly, Prairie Schooner, Indiana Review, Hayden's Ferry Review,* and elsewhere.

Through their primordiality, intuition and dream logic, permission to reject genre boundaries, and the way that they pull spellwork out of one's unconscious, fairy tales continue to hold dominion over my words.

PRESTON SMITH holds an MA in English literature and writes poetry and fiction. His work appears in *Thin Air Magazine, Tilde,* and *Perhappened,* among other publications.

Fairy tales have given me hope since I was a child, and they later became ways to express myself and my emotions, as well as the focus of my research in graduate school. They're my forever love.

ADDIE TSAI is a queer nonbinary artist and writer of color who teaches at the College of William & Mary. They have an MFA in Creative Writing from Warren Wilson College and a PhD in Dance from Texas Woman's University. They are the author of the queer Asian young adult novel *Dear Twin*. *Unwieldy Creatures* is their newly released adult queer nonbinary biracial Asian retelling of *Frankenstein*. They are Founding Editor & Editor-in-Chief at *just femme & dandy*.

I first encountered "The Little Mermaid" as I imagined many of us did—through the loosely inspired Disney animated adaptation. I was ten, the perfect age to come upon the buxom redhead with the voice of silk, alongside her crustacean companion. I came to understand my own childhood circumstances more clearly through that film, as a child of a dominant Asian father who didn't understand my desire to be in the world. I, too, would have bartered almost anything of mine in order to be free. As I grew older, I studied Hans Christian Andersen's original and Yayoi Kusama's hauntingly illustrated edition. Even though I would learn that the overbearing father was not quite the same in the original as he was in Disney's recreation, there was still something about the little mermaid's need to become human and leave her family behind that I deeply resonated with. As I've come to understand my own gender fluidity and nonbinary identity, "The Little Mermaid" has bloomed open for me, revealing layers I hadn't seen before.

MICHAEL VARGAS is a queer Chicano who earned degrees in English and Anthropology as a first-generation college student. He comes from a family of field laborers, mechanics, and blue-collar workers in Southern California, where he still lives and works as a mail carrier and writes poems.

My poems document my experience as a queer Chicano, weaving in the stories and histories of my family. I often draw imagery from fairy tales, magic, and mythology because they help transcend a world that is not built to hold individuals like me. Through them, I can explore the ways gender and sexuality conflict with tradition and expectations, linger in moments in my family's history when individuals weren't given choices, and rescript their stories to provide new agency.

JAE TOWLE VIEIRA is a writer and editor from rural Northern California. Their fiction has been published in *The Normal School, New England Review, Carve Magazine, Passages North, Mississippi Review*, and elsewhere. They are the editor of Manzanita Papers.

I'm interested in the forms of fairy tales—how their shells can be cast off, reinhabited, warped. I'm interested in the ways we pass forms to one another, how we convey the difference between insides and outsides, truths and dogmas, wilds and homes. Fairy tales function as the seam between the conscious and the unconscious and evoke the mindset I'm always trying to cultivate when I write: a knowing not-knowing.